THE ST. LAWRENCE
SEAWAY

THE ST. LAWRENCE
SEAWAY

BY THE HON. LIONEL CHEVRIER M.P.

ST MARTIN'S PRESS   NEW YORK   1959

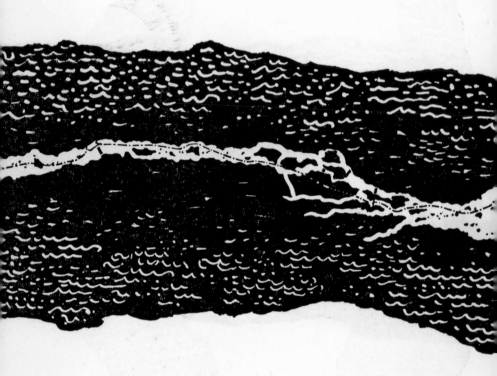

Copyright, Canada, 1959, by Lionel Chevrier

Printed and bound in Canada
by T. H. Best Printing Company Limited

Designed by Frank Davies, MTDC

To my wife and children

OTTAWA

1959

The idea of writing the story of the St. Lawrence Seaway
has long been in my mind. It is only now that it has come
to fruition. Over the years I have gathered a great deal of
material on the subject. I began as early as 1928, when I
became greatly attracted to the project in my capacity as
Secretary of the Board of Trade of the City of Cornwall
situated in the heart of the International Section. I continued to do so after I became the Member of Parliament
for the constituency of Stormont in 1935. Much of the
information contained in this book was compiled in such
manner. Much of it was obtained in my capacity as
Minister of Transport (1945-54), but the greatest part
as President of the St. Lawrence Seaway (1954-57).

I have derived a great deal of pleasure from putting
this story together. Because of my close association with
the project for over twelve years, I was, I believe, in a
particularly good position to see what was happening, to
follow the events from day to day and to judge of these
as they came across my desk.

Since most of the information here set forth was obtained while I was a servant of the Crown, I have felt
that I should not profit from the sale of the book. So I
have authorized a trust company to see that any proceeds
derived from my royalties be paid over to the Red Cross

Society in Ottawa and "La Corvée du Cardinal" in Montreal, in equal shares.

I could not have completed this work alone. I am indebted to many people. Mr. R. A. C. Henry, Consulting Engineer, was of great assistance to me. When the project became a reality, his advice was given unhesitatingly although he was not then a servant of the government. It was invaluable. I am grateful to Mr. Charles Gavsie, former President of the Seaway Authority, Mr. J.-C. Lessard, Vice-President of the Seaway Authority, Mr. Ernest Côté, Assistant Deputy Minister of Northern Affairs and National Resources, Mr. George Scott, Director of Economic Policy, Department of Transport, and Mr. W. M. Sprung, who was particularly helpful in the early stages, for reading the manuscript and for their many helpful suggestions. To Mr. Frank Russell, without whose editorial assistance the completion of this book would not have been possible, I express my gratitude. To my secretaries in the Seaway Authority, Miss Annette Leblanc and Miss Gladys Mainguy, to my present secretary Mrs. Lyône Boult, and to Mrs. Theresa Fawcett and Miss Colleen O'Shea who spent many long hours typing drafts of this volume, I offer my thanks.

I hope the reader will find this book profitable.

Lionel Chevrier

CONTENTS

PREFACE   vi

LIST OF MAPS AND PICTURES   ix

CHAPTER ONE: THE ST. LAWRENCE   2
            The Idea of a Seaway
            The Great River

CHAPTER TWO: EARLY PIONEERS   14
            De Casson's Dream
            Vision of Cantin
            The Canal-Builders
            The Energy of William Hamilton Merritt
            The Example of Erie
            The Quickest Route to the Sea?
            The Third and Last Stage

CHAPTER THREE: WHITE POWER   28
            Hydro-Electric Development
            The Valley's Potential
            The Great Power Plan

CHAPTER FOUR: THE ALL-CANADIAN SEAWAY   42
            Seizing the Initiative
            The U.S. Comes In
            Work Begins

CHAPTER FIVE: CONSTRUCTION BEGINS   58
            Working Together
            On the Job

CHAPTER SIX: THE WORK GOES FORWARD   80
     Excavation
     Lachine Construction
     Drying Up the Rapids
     Construction of the Power Project
     Thousand Islands and the Welland

CHAPTER SEVEN: MOVING THE PEOPLE   102
     One Hundred Square Miles Expropriated
     Persuading the Iroquois
     Moving Old Settlements
     The Models

CHAPTER EIGHT: THE BATTLE OF THE TOLLS   114
     The Question of Toll Rates
     Surprise Over Welland
     Practical Details

CHAPTER NINE: EFFECTS OF THE SEAWAY   126
     Old Anxieties
     A Glimpse of the Future
     Montreal's Reaction
     St. Lawrence Traffic Jam?

CHAPTER TEN: THE EIGHTH SEA   140
     Looking Back
     Achievement at Last

INDEX   147

MAPS AND PICTURES   151

MAP: WESTERN SECTION / WELLAND TO PRESCOTT 151
MAP: CENTRAL SECTION / IROQUOIS TO CORNWALL 152
MAP: EASTERN SECTION / LAKE ST. FRANCIS
          TO MONTREAL 153
Entrance to the Seaway: Montreal 154
Diagram: raising the Jacques Cartier Bridge 155
St. Lambert Lock and Victoria Bridge 156
Diagram: traffic flow at St. Lambert Lock 157
Seaway Channel west of Côte Ste. Catherine 158
Honoré Mercier and Caughnawaga Bridges 159
At the foot of Lake St. Louis 160
Beauharnois (1) 161
Beauharnois (2) 162
Seaway officials on inspection tour 163
The new Cornwall International High-Level Bridge 163
The International Power Project 164
MAP: THE INTERNATIONAL SECTION 166
Preparing for "Inundation Day" 167
The lock and dam at Iroquois 168
Moving the people: Iroquois 170
Persuading the Iroquois 171
Moving the people: Morrisburg 172
Model of the Cornwall area 173
The Welland Canal 174

credits 174

THE ST. LAWRENCE

SEAWAY

BY LIONEL CHEVRIER

CHAPTER ONE

THE ST. LAWRENCE

The Idea of a Seaway

The Great River

THE IDEA OF A SEAWAY

When my father was a young man living at Ste. Anne de Bellevue, Quebec, he visited his brother-in-law at Cornwall, Ontario. The visit changed my father's life. His brother-in-law was an accountant with a company building a canal at Cornwall to by-pass the Long Sault Rapids. He was excited by the opportunities the canal would bring to the town and he communicated much of his excitement to my father. For days after he returned to Ste. Anne's, where he worked in a general store, he kept saying, "If I could only get to Cornwall, I'm sure my fortune would be made."

The Cornwall canal was an insignificant affair by modern standards, 14 feet deep and capable of taking ships loaded with little more than 1,000 tons of cargo. Cornwall, too, was insignificant, with a population of less than 3,000. But my father could see this small canal bringing freight, industry and opportunity to Cornwall.

After many delays, he moved there in 1890 and found

the opportunities he had dreamed about. He became a successful business man, owning a moderately prosperous coal and lumber merchant's establishment on Cornwall's main street. The canal undoubtedly helped to make him successful with its cheap freight rates on coal. He became a town councillor, was elected mayor and narrowly missed being elected to the House of Commons. He did not live to see Cornwall become a great city. But its growth, spurred by that small canal, was prodigious. In my memory, it has increased from 5,000 to more than 45,000.

It is curious how the St. Lawrence River shaped the life of my father and later affected my own. In my youth, the river was useful for swimming and boating but I would have denied that it was influencing my future. My friends and I would sometimes go up-river to Sheek Island where there was a sandy beach within sight of the Long Sault Rapids. My family would frequently take the

3

The Idea of a Seaway

launch and go east down the river to a summer cottage my father kept on one of the islands in Lake St. Francis about twelve miles from Cornwall.

The river had no particular significance for me until I was in my teens, even though I can vaguely recall, about 1908, discussions about a "St. Lawrence waterway" among adults visiting our house. It really was not until I had completed my university education and had started a career with a Cornwall law firm that the drama and scope of the St. Lawrence River began to grip my imagination.

At this time, the mid-1920s, the river was much used by canallers, small river vessels which drew less than fourteen feet of water and which could be lifted by the existing canal system past the various rapids. These vessels ran between Montreal and Toronto. As I saw them loading and unloading at Cornwall, I began to understand the idea of the "St. Lawrence Waterway". This river, in effect, was a huge marine highway which provided the cheapest transportation possible for thousands of tons of goods every week. But the ships using it were too small. Much time was wasted as lake carriers unloaded at terminal points and the canallers reloaded for points east.

Ideally, this waste should be eliminated by allowing lake carriers to come down to Montreal and conversely allowing the sea-going ships, with their tens of thousands of tons of cargo, to enter the canals and reach the Great Lakes.

I began to understand how the river was being wasted in another way. Frequently in the summer, I would pass the Long Sault Rapids, which lay just west of Cornwall. As I grew older, I began to appreciate how these rapids were less a barrier to navigation than a waste of electric power. If the rapids could be dammed and a power-house built, Cornwall could become a centre of industry with abundant cheap power.

None of my ideas were original. Certainly none of

4

The St. Lawrence

them were new. For at least two hundred years before me, men had dreamed of a channel that would let large ships into the inland sea of North America—the Great Lakes. I learned that the Ontario Hydro Electric Power Commission had engineers surveying the St. Lawrence River at Cornwall before World War I to see how they might develop the power there.

But in one respect I was able to make a special contribution to the concept of a deep-water channel from the ocean to the Great Lakes. Largely because I was born by the river, brought up there and was always specially interested in it. I later became president of the St. Lawrence Seaway Authority, the Canadian Crown company which built two-thirds of the existing waterway. For three strenuous, worrying years, I handled this task and I count these years among the most stimulating in my life.

There never has been a time when two nations have co-operated to produce works of such size. The seaway was the most controversial construction project the world has known. It was one of the most ambitious and effective man-made alterations to the face of the earth ever completed. It outranks Suez or Panama in size.

Few projects have been so bitterly opposed or inspired so many opinions, arguments, legal battles, treaties and inter-government memoranda. Few projects have been so desperately needed while being delayed for so long. The seaway story is a chronicle of men fighting for self interest against nations fighting for national interest.

Before construction began, the real meaning and function of the seaway was buried under a mountain of words, written and spoken. A quick look at any file on the seaway project reveals a great mass of contradictory material. The seaway, this material reveals, will make Montreal wealthy, or it will drive it bankrupt. It may lower the price of coal: it may raise the price of coal. It will be far too big, although another point of view says that it will be much too small. It is rare to find a dis-

5

passionate observer of the seaway. It was a huge project which not only excited man's imagination but inflamed his emotions.

Briefly, the St. Lawrence Seaway consists of a 27-foot-deep channel which was dug through dry land and dredged through lake bottoms, stretching from Montreal to Lake Erie and capable of lifting most of the world's ships about 600 feet from sea level while they sail 2,000 miles inland. Conversely, it will allow lake carriers to come down to Montreal and other St. Lawrence River ports. It replaces a 14-foot-deep system of canals.

It will lower freight rates, change transportation methods. It will help to create the greatest concentration of industry in the world, much of it in Canada. It will make the U.S. and Canada even more interdependent than they are now. It may not lessen the importance of New York but it will certainly help Montreal, Chicago and Toronto to become as large as New York. It will have effects on the economy of the continent which will occupy the attention of economists for years to come. The seaway has given Canada a south coast stretching half-way across the nation.

THE GREAT RIVER

The St. Lawrence River, key to the inland sea of the Great Lakes and to the seaway, is a broad, beautiful stretch of water which has captured the imagination of politicians, poets and business men. It is the hero of the seaway story. Unlike other rivers of its size, it has not spread itself out. It is a tractable river, little inclined to flood. It drains roughly 700,000 square miles, an area twice that of France.

From Quebec to its mouth, it is more than one hundred feet deep, although navigation is complicated by numerous shoals. Its average width is two miles and it is nearly two thousand miles long. Such is its length and diver-

6

The St. Lawrence

sity, that it does not maintain its name for its full length. Between Lakes Superior and Huron it is called St. Mary's River—site of the famous Sault Ste. Marie Canal—and becomes St. Clair River between Lake Huron and Lake St. Clair.

It changes to Detroit River between Lake St. Clair and Lake Erie and to Niagara between Erie and Ontario. Despite its many changes of name, it is basically the same river, the drainage channel for nearly 100,000 square miles of the Great Lakes.

But the river and the lakes it passes through are dwarfed by the basin in which all of them flow. The basin's northerly rim extends from the middle of the North American continent right out to Labrador. This basin is, in effect, an enormous hollow dug out or formed during the glacial ages when thick ice covered much of the continent. At points along the St. Lawrence River today, traces of this áge can be seen. Drift grooves can be seen cut into hard granite, eighteen inches deep and thirty or forty feet long. As one writer put it, "A block of granite as large as a small house held fast in the undersurface of a moving sheet of ice has a glazier's diamond in its steel handle; another sheet of ice, hundreds of feet thick and thousands of miles wide and creeping onward with a slow but irresistible movement—what a glass-cutter that must have been!"

During this icy period, the glaciers pulverized billions of tons of rock into fine soil and deposited it over most of southern Ontario, Quebec and northern Michigan. After the ice had gone, the rough holes and hollows filled with water and the water began finding its way down to the sea. What was left was to become the heart of Canada.

It is difficult to form a clear mental image of this river-dominated area because it is so enormous, so diverse. For instance, for a number of years before the seaway was built, more traffic passed through the Soo Canal in one year than through Panama and Suez combined. Toronto

7

is the fastest-growing city in the world. Ontario's gross national product increased 200 per cent between 1946 and 1956. Duluth-Superior is the second largest port in the United States. Rich forest lands occur throughout. There are copious deposits of iron, silver, copper, zinc, lead and nickel. The lakes teem with pike, pickerel, bass, sturgeon, carp and perch. Enormous reserves of natural gas are being unleashed on the shores of Lake Erie.

Dominating these facts and figures is the river itself. Officially, it begins at Kingston, Ontario, where Lake Ontario water begins its run to the sea, and it ends a thousands miles away, at the Strait of Belle Isle. In my youth, I knew the river well, of course, although I never dreamed that I would help to change parts of it beyond recognition. Fortunately, the most beautiful part of it remains unchanged. From Kingston to Prescott, it wanders among myriads of islands. This stretch of water, sixty miles long, is known as the Thousand Islands. It is sometimes called the Venice of America.

There are islands of every size, hardly one without summer homes of city dwellers. There are imposing mansions, palatial country clubs, simple cottages. Some islands are only slightly bigger than the cottages perched on them. Motor cruisers, yachts, small boats and seaplanes are moored to jetties. On one island is an uncompleted castle which, as originally planned by a rich American, was to have had fifty bathrooms, Westminster chimes, a pipe organ, Italian gardens, carvings, mosaics, tapestries and works of art, fountains, elevators and swimming pools.

Every island has some historical story to tell. During the patriot wars of 1837-8, the famous river pirate Bill Johnston boarded a steamer at Wellesley Island, ordered all the passengers ashore and set fire to the ship. It drifted off, struck a shoal and sank in a gout of flame and steam. Johnston was supposed to have hidden on an island in a small cave called Devil's Oven, with his

8

The St. Lawrence

daughter Kate acting as a watchdog. Although eventually captured, he escaped after six months and was later pardoned, to become the new lighthouse keeper on Rock Island. An ill-advised Colonel von Schoultz led six hundred men in an invasion of Canada along this stretch of the river. But the U.S. Government seized his invasion fleet, the Canadians beleaguered him in an old windmill and he and his lieutenants were hanged at Kingston.

At Prescott, before the seaway was built, there was a natural rock barrier which controlled the level of Lake Ontario. The water spilled over this and began its long steady fall down the International Rapids section of the river. Specially built cargo-ships called "lakers" used to stop at Prescott, unload their 10,000-ton cargoes of grain into a giant elevator, which transferred them to smaller shallow-draughted "canallers". During the War of 1812, Prescott was the headquarters of Colonel "Red" George Macdonell, commander of the Canadian Scottish militia there. He became famous for his feinted attacks across the ice in winter at Ogdensburg on the American side. The American garrison became bored by the peculiar British tactics and were ill prepared for the unexpected ferocity and suddenness of the real attack which crumbled the defences quickly.

Macdonell once received word that Montreal was menaced by a large force of Americans. He put six hundred men into boats and started down the river. There was no time to get a pilot, so the colonel took the helm of the lead boat. A dozen near escapes and a fierce storm did not slow the colonel, and his six hundred men reached Montreal without loss and helped to defeat the Americans.

The International Rapids—Galops (pronounced "Galloos"), Rapide Plat, Farran's Point, and the Long Sault —disappeared with the construction of the seaway. Little did we know as youngsters that Sheek Island, our favourite swimming-place, would one day lie deep under water with only its topknot showing. The rapids in those days

9

stretched over forty miles of river and dropped ninety feet towards the sea.

Freight-carrying vessels rarely shot the rapids but pleasure ships took passengers down this section of the river daily. Guides and members of ships' crews tried to stimulate excitement over the dangers of shooting the rapids and a Murray Bay blanket was usually raffled afterwards. As I remember those trips, there was not a great deal of danger, but the white-capped waves, the hiss and roar of roiling water, created an excellent illusion of it, and occasionally a ship did get stuck.

The Long Sault Rapids were particularly exciting. One traveller, Henry Beston, described his steamer trip down the Long Sault as being "A shudder, a strange motion downhill into a vast confusion and a vaster sound. . . ." At times, travellers seemed to be sweeping downstream in a trough, the banks of the river obscured by walls of water.

The first large steamer to go down the rapids was the *Ontario*, which was built at Niagara about 1840. She was bought as a mail-boat to operate between Montreal and Quebec. Two Indian pilots, Old Jock and Old Pete, were offered $1,000 to bring the ship safely to Montreal. They built a ship's dummy hull, forty feet long, riding ten feet deep in the water. This dummy shot the rapids, closely watched by the two Indians who later easily imitated the feat with the real ship.

I have heard much talk of the great rafts of timber that used to be floated down the river toward the end of the nineteenth century. Floating islands of wood, built by French Canadians and called "drams", were 60 feet wide and up to 350 feet long. A raft of "drams" could be 1,500 feet long and contain cabins, kitchens, boats, tools and oars. A hundred people might travel by dram down the river, and travellers would be entertained by the raftmen singing French-Canadian songs. Each dram was equipped with 30-foot oars for controlling the unwieldy masses of wood in the rapids. A steam tug usually took

10

The St. Lawrence

control of the drams, which were so long that the raftmen could see the tug suddenly disappear from sight as it plunged down the steepest rapids.

At the foot of where the Long Sault Rapids used to be is Cornwall, where I was born. Below it is Lake St. Francis, 26 miles long and about 100 feet below Lake Ontario, and about 150 feet above sea level. At the end of the lake the river quickly goes through another series of rapids—Coteau, Cedars, Split Rock and Cascades—and spills into Lake St. Louis. This is the Soulanges section of the river, mainly notable for the enormous Beauharnois Power Canal down which a large part of the river's flow was diverted when the Beauharnois power-house was built in 1932. This man-made canal, 3,300 feet wide, 30 feet deep and 15 miles long, took more excavating than the Panama Canal and is now a part of the seaway navigation channel.

Lake St. Louis, which is merely an enlargement of the river of thirteen miles, leads into the Lachine Rapids. They have the worst reputation of any of the fast waters along the river. This applies with almost equal force to the Cedars and the Cascades, the Rapids between Lake St. Francis and Lake St. Louis, where General Amherst, running these rapids in 1760, lost forty-six of his boats carrying supplies and military stores, and eighty-four men drowned. General Frederick Haldimand, who saw the disaster, resolved that he would prevent such a thing happening again. When he became Governor of Quebec in 1778, he began building a series of small locks, on the south side of the river, between Lake St. Francis and Lake St. Louis. These were among the early beginnings of the seaway.

Mrs. John Graves Simcoe went down the Lachine Rapids in 1796 and noted in her diary that ". . . the great width of the river adds terror to the scene, which represents miles of foaming waves. We stopped a little while, that we might not overtake or run foul of an immense

11

The Great River

radeau or raft that was going down. However, she struck a rock and we passed her."

T. R. Glover and D. D. Calvin, two Kingston men, once wrote how they shot the Lachine on a dram. "Presently, the long dram undulated over the first smooth rounded waves of the rapids, a moment more and we had fairly entered. As the dram hit the first big waves of the sharper descent the steersmen hauled in their oars and ran back to escape the water as it boiled over the bow of the dram, whose whole fabric bent and strained to conform to the long waves of the rapids—we dashed down the main 'pitch' in what seemed no more than a few seconds. There was a curious illusion that the great barely submerged rocks were rushing upstream as we passed them; the heavy timber bumped and thudded underfoot, the water spurted up in great jets as the sides of two pieces of it struck flat together."

At the foot of the rapids lies Montreal Harbour, where Jacques Cartier paused in 1536 and looked up the Lachine Rapids. Like many others after him, his mind was excited by the possibility of being able to sail farther and farther up the river and eventually reach the inland sea, perhaps even reach China—La Chine.

12

The St. Lawrence

CHAPTER TWO

EARLY PIONEERS

De Casson's Dream

Vision of Cantin

The Canal-Builders

The Energy of William Hamilton Merritt

The Example of Erie

The Quickest Route to the Sea?

The Third and Last Stage

DE CASSON'S DREAM

Two hundred and fifty years ago, a burly citizen of New France stood on a bank overlooking the Lachine Rapids. He was Dollier de Casson, Superior of the Sulpician seminary, a former soldier of such strength that he could hold two men aloft at once, one in each hand. He was also one of the hardiest pioneers of early Canada, and had endured great hardships to penetrate the wild country hundreds of miles to the west. As he watched the rapids, he was forming a plan that would take French ships of commerce up the St. Lawrence River into the lakes which he knew lay beyond. The ships would bring missionaries, settlers, trappers, business men, craftsmen, traders. They would take furs, grain, lumber.

Dollier de Casson's plan was to build a canal that would by-pass the rapids. But such was the size of this project, and such was the uncertainty of life in the new colony—the Iroquois murdered two hundred French settlers in a terrible attack in 1689—that he had to wait

14

Early Pioneers

nearly twenty years to sign a construction contract for the building of the Canal de la Chine. He had to fight strong opposition from his superiors, both in New France and in European France. Only his energy and drive kept the idea alive of a canal to the "inland seas" of the Great Lakes. When he died in 1701, with only a 2,000-yard dyke excavated from a seminary mill on the Rivière St. Pierre, it was found that he had spent 20,000 livres on the project, an enormous sum for New France in those days.

The idea of being able to sail a ship from the Atlantic Ocean deep into the heart of North America is more than 300 years old. Jacques Cartier thought of it in 1536. It was a fascinating and baffling fact to all early explorers and developers of Canada that the magnificent St. Lawrence—so broad, so deep, so eminently navigable—should suddenly degenerate into fierce rapids at key points along its course.

De Casson's Dream

This feeling of bafflement increased as the years went by. As the explorers were followed by commerce, it became supremely frustrating that it was not possible to load grain at Duluth and sail it to Amsterdam; or load textiles at Liverpool and unload them at Chicago. To Europeans, it was as annoying as if the Mediterranean were sealed off completely from the Atlantic at Gibraltar.

The rapids that blocked the explorers and men of commerce were caused by the St. Lawrence falling 600 feet from the head of the Great Lakes to the sea. All the Great Lakes are different heights above sea level. Superior, Michigan, Huron and Erie are all between 570 and 600 feet above the sea, Ontario only 245 feet.

It is not surprising that from the time Dollier de Casson's men first dug shovels into the Canal de la Chine, till the St. Lawrence Seaway was officially opened in June, 1959, there was an almost constant battle to develop a deep channel for ocean-going ships into the Great Lakes.

VISION OF CANTIN

When I was a youngster in Cornwall, Ontario, a visitor to my father's office from time to time could be heard talking lengthily and excitedly about the "St. Lawrence waterway". I can only vaguely remember this man now. I doubt whether I met him more than a dozen times but I did notice that he had a great capacity for making people listen and agree with what he was saying. At that time, I did not realize who Narcisse Cantin was, or how he fitted into the St. Lawrence Seaway project.

Cantin is a symbol of all the disappointments that preceded the seaway. He had more than his share of them. He was as much of a visionary as Dollier de Casson and it was hardly his fault that he failed to realize any of his dreams of the seaway.

He came from a boat-building family who lived in a

16

Early Pioneers

French settlement on the shores of Lake Huron. He closely resembled Dollier de Casson in size, standing well over six feet and weighing about 240 pounds. He was impatient, and early in life broke away from the boat-building tradition to become a cattle buyer and trader. He married at seventeen and set out on a life of adventure. He was once a sparring partner for John L. Sullivan. He invented a new type of furniture polish and patented a new model of gas burner.

At some point in his varied and adventurous life, he became obsessed with canals. One of his heroes was William Paterson, the brilliant Scotsman who tried to build Panama in 1698—an almost Jules Verne-like attempt on the future. Cantin was fascinated by Paterson's success in securing a charter from the Scottish Parliament for a "Company of Scotland trading to Africa and the Indies". This company was to build a town at Darien, on the Panamanian Isthmus, dig a canal and "thus hold the key to the commerce of the world and turn Scotland from one of the poorest to one of the richest countries".

In 1919, some years after I had first seen Cantin in Cornwall, he published a booklet in which he outlined his plan to build a thirty-foot waterway connecting Lakes Champlain, Ontario, Erie, Huron, Michigan and Superior. A thirty-foot canal! When at last we built the seaway, we only made it twenty-seven feet deep. Cantin's ideas were bigger than those of his age.

He wanted to see $500 million spent on navigational works, $200 million on "hydraulic development". He planned a canal running from Lake Champlain due west to the St. Lawrence. He wanted a new canal to replace the Welland. He planned a 43-mile canal running overland between Lakes Erie and Huron and by-passing Detroit and Windsor. He planned a network of canals running through the rapids sections of the St. Lawrence. He wanted more canals joining the Ottawa and St. Lawrence Rivers.

For a private individual to suggest a project of such

17

magnitude at that time was hardly less visionary than Paterson's Panama canal idea and it is not surprising that there was little enthusiasm for it. But being a show-man and promoter at heart, he immediately decided that he needed some promotional device to attract public attention. It would have to be big enough to create public confidence. There must be no suggestion that this was created by an opportunist who wanted to make a quick profit.

Cantin moved in on the Ontario village of Johnson's Mills, renamed it St. Joseph and set out to build a sea-way city. He established local industry, including a lumber mill, an organ-pipe factory and a novelty factory. A reporter from the London *Free Press* visited Cantin's young city in September, 1897, and wrote a four-page report extolling the development. With the town under way, Cantin travelled almost continuously between Montreal and New York, hunting up the money that he needed, ostensibly to build a new industrial city, but in fact to begin the construction of his thirty-foot channel to the Great Lakes.

In 1898, he applied to Ottawa for a charter to build his canal. Ottawa turned him down. He tried again in 1902, 1903, 1904, but without success. He campaigned tirelessly among business men, politicians and men in the shipping business. He harped on the theme that his sea-way would cause a revolution. "We should not fail to appreciate the significance of having ocean vessels flying the flags of all nations of the world," he would say grand-ly, "carrying passengers and freight from all ocean ports on the globe direct to all the principal ports of the Great Lakes."

By comparison, he pointed out, the cost of creating the Great-Lakes-to-ocean route was less than and its importance as great as any of the existing "world-famous canals".

In his salesmanship and promotional efforts, Cantin so impressed Charles Schwab of Bethlehem Steel that

18

Early Pioneers

Schwab—instead of giving him money for the seaway—offered him a $100,000 job. But the seaway was an obsession with Cantin and he went on to incorporate the Great Lakes and Atlantic Canal and Power Company in 1914, which was intended to "create a public demand for a speedy navigable waterway".

But Cantin's efforts bogged down in a swamp of legalistic argument, red tape, indifference and hostility. The further he worked his way into the twentieth century, the less chance he had of personally achieving his aim. His idea was already beginning to excite the governments of the United States and Canada.

THE CANAL-BUILDERS

To reach the Great Lakes from the Atlantic, a canal is obviously necessary. But who could dream of a canal to lift an ocean-going ship 600 feet over 2,000 miles? When the St. Lawrence first occupied the attention of the canal-builders, Suez was barely a notion, Panama an impossibility. When Dollier de Casson first began digging near Lachine before 1700, there were no historical precedents for the job that lay ahead.

This was despite the fact that canal-building was almost as old as history itself. The Assyrians and Babylonians were digging huge canals a thousand or more years before Christ. The Egyptians and Greeks used them frequently. In Nero's time, the Romans tried to build the Corinth Canal. The Chinese built the enormous Grand Canal, 650 miles long and five feet deep from Hang-chau to Tientsin. But these canals had no locks. The lock was invented only a couple of hundred years before de Casson.

So it is doubtful whether any of the early developers could see much hope of a deep channel with locks leading all the way to the Great Lakes. The initial efforts of

19

canal-builders were to create the smallest type of channels to accommodate the smallest river vessels.

The Royal Engineers built four small canals between 1779 and 1783 on the north shore of the river, to avoid the rapids between Lake St. Louis and Lake St. Francis. But nobody could say that the building of the canals was the result of the work of far-sighted visionaries who wanted to begin developing the centre of the continent. Their construction was a strategic necessity, caused by fear that the American revolutionary war might spread to Canada. The canals, which had the first locks on the river—and perhaps in North America—were only two feet six inches deep and the locks barely six feet wide.

De Casson's dream was finally realized in 1824 when a five-foot-deep Lachine Canal was completed by a government commission which took over the work from the Lachine Canal Company when it got into difficulties. All this canal-building was merely nibbling at the big objective.

THE ENERGY OF WILLIAM HAMILTON MERRITT

Because of the huge scale of the St. Lawrence Seaway idea, men of great vision, energy and persistence were needed to keep it alive. Perhaps the first of these men after Dollier de Casson was W. Hamilton Merritt. He was born in the United States in 1793 and his father, Thomas Merritt, came to Canada when young Merritt was three, leaving behind a family tradition of freehold farming in Westchester County in New York. Young Merritt fought against the Americans in the War of 1812, was captured and spent till March, 1815, in a Massachusetts prisoner-of-war camp, when he returned to his home in Upper Canada.

He was known along the Niagara Peninsula as a man of extraordinary energy and drive and his activities on returning from the war certainly seemed to prove this.

20

Early Pioneers

By 1816, he had a store, a farm, a sawmill, a flour mill, a distillery, a potashery, a cooper shop, and a smithy, all of which he built from practically nothing. He used money earned from the lucrative flour business to pay his debts and expand as quickly as possible.

Merritt's property was on the banks of Twelve Mile Creek which discharged into Lake Ontario about 15 miles west of Niagara. He was worried because the creek did not supply a regular flow of water for his various mills. A sudden flood, on the other hand, could destroy his equipment and bankrupt him.

On September 18, 1818, Merritt borrowed a water-level from a friend and set out with some neighbours, mostly millers like himself, to find out whether it was feasible to tap water from the Welland River, which ran west to east into the Niagara almost due south of his own property. Between Merritt and the Welland was a high ridge, through which the Twelve Mile Creek had cut a ravine. The creek ended a couple of miles short of the Welland itself.

Nobody is quite sure what happened during this surveying expedition but it is known that Merritt, a notoriously impatient man, mismeasured the height of the ridge. He recorded it as thirty feet. (Actually, it is closer to sixty feet.) Whether or not Merritt and his friends were elated because the ridge seemed so low they appear to have become fired with a grand idea: Why not build a ship-carrying canal that would join both lakes?

The men moved fast. On October 14, a petition was made to the legislature of Upper Canada appealing for the construction of a canal between Lakes Erie and Ontario. The petition said in part: "The grand object of the American people appears to be opening a navigation with Lake Erie, which design, our canal, if effected soon, would counteract; and take down the whole of the produce from the western country."

But despite Merritt's best efforts, the proposal did not

21

gain favour with the legislators and soon afterwards he went bankrupt. But he recovered and five years later, after promoting a long and tremendously expensive series of government surveys—none of which envisaged using Twelve Mile Creek for the canal—he suggested a plan for a privately built canal. It was to run from Lake Ontario to the Welland River and was to be four feet deep, like the recently completed Erie Canal. Merritt secured a charter from the Lieutenant-Governor to build it in 1823, and, with a capital of just £25,000 and eight provisional directors—of whom all except one owned land along Twelve Mile Creek—he set to work.

With hopelessly insufficient capital, with an initial survey that was hopelessly inaccurate, with a board of directors who knew practically nothing about engineering or canal-building, it is an extraordinary tribute to Merritt that once his construction started it never stopped till the job was done. The canal was dug seven feet six inches deep and was kept under way by massive helpings of extra capital raised by the tireless Merritt on trips all over the country.

The board of directors were responsible for some very persuasive promotional copy. In a report issued in 1825, they commented on the work of the Welland Canal Company: "No work in Europe or America will bear comparison with it in usefulness. In touching upon the mighty results which must soon follow its completion, the truth will assume the appearance of the most extravagant exaggeration, to those who do not make themselves acquainted with the singular geographical position of North America. . . . It is truly a national object and ought to be executed on a scale of unrivalled magnitude, at any cost, and at any trouble. It will be cheap at five times the estimated amount of £250,000."

At one stage, a Scots engineer named MacTaggart, who had been employed by the British Government to build the Rideau Canal to Ottawa, took one sour look at Merritt's wooden lock gates, compared them with the

22

Early Pioneers

massive masonry locks of his own canal, and said the whole Welland Canal would be swept into Lake Ontario "like a lot of birdcages" with the first freshet.

But Merritt would not be discouraged. His friends said of him that he was a man obsessed by a canal. Little else concerned him except this "Navigation of one hundred and six miles in length with an ascent of 358 feet, surmounted by forty wooden locks . . .", as he described the project.

The first ships to pass through the Welland Canal, on November 30, 1829, were two schooners; but the canal was in extremely bad shape because of the haste with which it had been completed. During construction, banks collapsed, dams disappeared, cholera swept through the labourers and much re-designing was necessary. Moreover, traffic through the canal was not so heavy as anticipated. In 1841, the government took over the Welland Canal Company and placed it under the control of the Board of Works.

THE EXAMPLE OF ERIE

While Merritt's canal was being built, the Erie Canal was completed in the United States. It was opened with some pomp, as befitted a project so important to the United States early in the nineteenth century. A fleet of vessels decorated with bunting set out with State dignitaries and began a triumphal voyage from Buffalo overland to New York City. Guns thundered a welcome to the fleet along the five hundred miles of its journey. At New York, Governor De Witt Clinton spilled a barrel of Lake Erie water into the ocean.

Even while the Welland was still being resolutely engineered against the most appalling difficulties, the Erie Canal began proving to the world how conspicuously the right canal in the right place could influence the

23

economy of hundreds of thousands of square miles of territory.

Before the Erie was built, the land between the east coast and the middle west had no cheap outlet to the sea. Goods had to be transported over the Ohio River to the Mississippi, a long, dangerous and expensive journey. Worse still, there was little incentive for incoming trade and only a trickle of goods came up the big river. For the grain producers on the western side of the Alleghenies, the freight rates over the mountains were impossibly high. It was jokingly said in those days that the only grain which could afford to make the trip was transported as whiskey.

But to observe the greatest effect of the Erie Canal, an observer would only need to visit Montreal. There was the deepest sort of gloom. Within months of the opening of the canal, it became apparent that Canada's greatest city had suffered a temporarily crippling economic blow. Canadian historian D. G. Creighton wrote of this period, ". . . Montreal, the incredible little city which had won half a continent, was now—what it had always seemed—a small provincial town." Montreal, in its fight to become the eastern port for the middle west, had been beaten by more energetic, better organized opponents. The New York merchants had watched Montreal's growing importance with mounting alarm. They foresaw what would happen to their city if Montreal captured the cheap freight route running nearly two thousand miles into the interior of their own continent.

But perhaps it is unfair to blame Montreal for this failure to seize an empire. It was an age of bitter rivalry between Upper and Lower Canada. The French-dominated assembly of Lower Canada was not sympathetic to the English merchant community. Moreover, there was a depression in 1819. The North West Company went out of business, merging with the Hudson's Bay Company in 1821, and so ended the St. Lawrence fur trade. Worst of all, the British Government was more

24

anxious to see canal improvements that would help keep the American military out of Canada than to encourage freight fights between rival business men. The British therefore improved the Rideau Canal between Kingston and Ottawa, and the merchants of Montreal suffered.

American farm products now reached the east coast in eight days, instead of three months down the Mississippi. A ton of corn from Northern Ohio could be shipped to New York for $10. The old, or Mississippi, price was $100. Small wonder the canal was jammed with freight almost from the day it was opened.

The example of Erie may have been a spur to Merritt, but it was also something much more important. It illustrated clearly the inevitability of the St. Lawrence Seaway. But one thing it did not indicate: The seaway was still more than 100 years away.

THE QUICKEST ROUTE TO THE SEA?

By the end of the eighteenth century, the St. Lawrence had established itself as the great Canadian freight route to the east. Wheat and lumber were urgently needed in Europe. In 1802, for instance, Canada exported about one million bushels of wheat, much of which came down the river. The St. Lawrence was becoming crowded with Durham boats, flat-bottomed, unwieldy craft carrying up to ten tons but well adapted to the primitive canals then in existence. Steamboats began running between Quebec and Montreal and the warehouses of the two cities were filled with wheat, flour, beef, lumber, biscuit and pork.

But once the Erie Canal was completed, the glittering prospect of this west-to-east movement of trade—all of it converging upon Montreal—vanished like a puff of smoke. For a while, an even more serious disaster seemed likely. The Erie threatened to split the two provinces, Upper Canada being drawn to New York by cheap freight rates. Upper Canada was impoverished and some-

25

what American in its outlook. It resented the French cultural, economic and political superiority. It had no seaport and received little or no investment money from the rich Montreal merchants.

Should the Erie Canal become central Canada's cheap outlet to the sea, the rich heart-land of the country would be reluctantly forced to entrust its millions of tons of freight to American carriers. What the War of 1812 had failed to do, the canny merchants of New York City might very well achieve without a shot being fired.

Fortunately, while the question of Upper Canada's independence went unanswered, Upper and Lower Canada united in 1841. The quickest and cheapest route to the sea through Canadian territory now became a necessity. The Lachine Canal at Montreal was rebuilt by 1848. The Beauharnois Canal was finished in 1845, the Cornwall Canal in 1843. The second Welland Canal was completed in 1846. These works were not built by soldiers for strategic purposes. Their engineers were civilians, and their construction heralded the commercial revolution that was approaching, if a little slowly.

So by 1848, there was a continuous channel never less than nine feet deep stretching from Lake Erie to Montreal. It had cost a little more than $15 million. For those who had finished the work, it seemed a time to lean back and wait for the boom. To many, it even seemed likely that the new canal system—an embryo seaway—would divert a good deal of U.S. traffic. In 1834, the Welland Canal shipped 40,000 bushels of wheat for Montreal and nearly 250,000 bushels for the Erie Canal which had a branch connection to Lake Ontario. The new Canadian channel did not alter these figures. The Erie had been getting the biggest share of the freight and continued to do so, a share soon to be lost to the railroads rather than to Canada's canals.

26

Early Pioneers

At first glance, a nine-foot channel from the Atlantic Ocean to Detroit and Windsor seems a great asset. But there were severe drawbacks, many of them caused by competition from the railroads. Water transport is cheap only if large cargoes are carried over long distances. Vessels with only nine-foot draught found it difficult to compete with rail freight. Since the canals were ice-bound for five months of the year, it was essential that during the relatively short freight season the maximum tonnage should be carried.

So, in effect, the work of modernization had to be done over again. The Lachine and Welland were deepened once more, this time to fourteen feet. A new canal was built at Cornwall, and this was the one which excited my father so much. A magnificent deep-channel canal was built by the Americans at Sault Ste. Marie.

The result of this tremendous expansion was that by 1904, a fourteen-foot channel ran all the way from Montreal to Lake Erie. Connecting channels had been built between Lakes Erie and Huron and through the Canadian Sault Canal to the head of the Great Lakes. Only one task remained before the seaway as we know it today became feasible. It was the rebuilding of the Welland Ship Canal. It proved one of the greatest canal-building undertakings in the world. Construction was completed by 1932 at a cost of $132 million.

By 1937, the U.S. and Canada could have completed the deep-water channel to the ocean. Had the two countries acted as soon as the Welland was completed, the coming war might have been shortened and billions of dollars would certainly have been saved.

The seaway, it must again be emphasized, is a gigantic project. It was too big for the thinking of the early thirties. It was certainly too big for government pocketbooks. By the time the two countries might have been ready to go ahead with the project, they were at war with Germany and Japan.

27

The Third and Last Stage

CHAPTER THREE

WHITE POWER

Hydro-Electric Development

The Valley's Potential

The Great Power Plan

HYDRO-ELECTRIC DEVELOPMENT

A huge hydro-electric power-house holds back 100 square miles of lake water two miles west of Cornwall, Ontario. It is, I imagine, the only major structure in the world that is divided in half by an international boundary line. The Robert H. Saunders power-house ends half-way between the Canadian and American shore and is joined to an identical power-house built by the New York State Power Authority. It was built to exploit 2,200,000 horsepower of water energy that had been eyed covetously by Ontario Hydro, and others, for nearly forty years.

The power-house shows a fine spirit of co-operation between Canada and the U.S. It also shows how without a desperate need for electric power in Ontario and New York State, the St. Lawrence Seaway might still be waiting to be built.

The need for electric power influenced nearly all the international discussions about the seaway from the 1930s on. An instance of this occurred during 1951

28

when I was Minister of Transport. The Canadian Government was then trying to secure an agreement with Ontario covering the development of power in the International Rapids section. This action did not anticipate the Americans joining us in this venture.

An agreement had been worked out, in which Prime Minister St. Laurent, C. D. Howe and myself had a hand, by which the Federal Government would dig the navigation channel and build the locks for the seaway if the Ontario Government would build power-houses and dams necessary to exploit all the electric power in the international section of the river. Accordingly, we invited Premier Frost to come to Ottawa with his colleagues, including the provincial secretary George Challies and representatives of the Ontario Hydro Electric Power Commission.

Early in the meeting, we came to an impasse over the expenditure of several million dollars for some construc-

29

Hydro-Electric Development

tional work. Both the Prime Minister and I felt the Federal Government should not have to pay. Premier Frost was adamant that the Government of Ontario should not pay. After we had argued back and forth for a while, Robert Saunders, who was chairman of Ontario Hydro, suddenly said, "This project cannot be delayed any longer. I'll pay for it."

Saunders was determined to get power from the river. When I was appointed president of the Seaway Authority in the middle of 1954, he called me from Toronto and said, "We may disagree over political questions [he was a Tory] but we'll agree over the Seaway."

Saunders became chairman of the electrical utility in 1948 and was well known in Ontario as a former mayor of Toronto and a forceful personality. After becoming chairman, he flew over the International Rapids in his airplane on an inspection trip of the St. Lawrence River. I understand he resolved at that time to harness the rapids for power. He became determined he would never make a speech without mention of harnessing the St. Lawrence's power potential. In countless speeches later, he never missed emphasizing how the power of the river could be made to work for the province.

He took the St. Lawrence power story from Toronto to Ottawa and from Ottawa to Washington. He became angry at American indecision. He once said, "The bickering in the United States over this project would be laughable if it were not so tragic. Never in the history of North America have we witnessed such a spectacle. Never were the private interests of a few so allowed to impede the progress and protection of two great countries. . . . The Canadian Government should say, 'Uncle Sam, we can't afford to wait any longer. Our people must be protected and the industrial progress of our country must not be impeded.' " He used to say in speeches that Ontario Hydro customers would have to pay $33 million more to buy steam-produced power than to have St. Lawrence-generated power. When the two

30

White Power

Governments finally agreed to begin the power project, Saunders already had 150 men working on the job, completely equipped with plans and surveys that were begun 18 months previously.

But ironically, like many before him—Cantin, de Casson, Merritt—Saunders was deprived of his moment of glory. He lived long enough to learn that the power-house would be named after him but he died in a crash of his plane in 1955 three and a half years before it began generating St. Lawrence power.

The building of the Robert H. Saunders power-house ended nearly half a century of efforts to develop hydro power near Cornwall. I can remember Narcisse Cantin making mention of "hydraulic power" at Cornwall long before World War I. The Ontario Hydro Electric Power Commission, formed in 1906, actually had its engineers surveying the International Rapids section in that year to see how hydro power might be developed there.

But the first real international effort to get power from the river was in 1920. And the effort had to be international. To get hydro power, you must dam the river somewhere, and this was only possible along the international boundary line. Two well known engineers, W. A. Bowden of Canada and Lieutenant-Colonel W. P. Wooten of the United States, were asked by Canada and the U.S. to report on the best methods of building the seaway, what effects it would have on each country, how it should be controlled and so on. The two men ranged up and down the river for more than a year, surveying, measuring, discussing, arguing and estimating. They produced such a definitive report that their names became synonymous with the seaway for the next thirty years.

They said a deep channel for ocean-going ships between Lake Ontario and Montreal was perfectly feasible. It would need nine locks, twenty-three miles of canal twenty-five feet deep. Hydro-electric power developed would be nearly 1,500,000 horsepower and would cost $252,728,000. The International Rapids section could

31

be easily by-passed by a series of dams and side canals. The whole project could be paid for within a few years by the revenue secured from the generation of power.

The report of the Joint Board of Engineers in 1926 was a monumental work, commissioned by the International Joint Commission, a body set up to deal with boundary disputes by a treaty in 1909 between Great Britain and the United States.

I never met either Wooten or Bowden, but I have spent many hours examining their report. It was one of the main documents that interested me when I came to the Department of Transport in 1945. It was a masterpiece of its kind, a report of monumental detail and meticulous accuracy. The charts attached to the report contain thousands of individual soundings along the river. Wooten and Bowden were working on this while I was taking my first year arts course at college.

Their report was followed by many others, most of which emphasized the vital part that power would play in any development. Like Wooten and Bowden, many engineers wanted the power to pay for the entire development. In March, 1930, the St. Lawrence Power Development Commission was created by the New York State Legislature. This commission, later to be called the Power Authority of the State of New York, was to be responsible for building power-houses along the St. Lawrence, in co-operation with whatever similar Canadian body was chosen for the job.

Even at that time, there were high hopes that construction of the seaway would start soon. The Great Lakes Waterway Treaty, signed in 1932, looked like getting the work started for a while but missed by twenty-six votes being ratified by the U.S. Senate. The Great Lakes-St. Lawrence Basin Agreement was signed in 1941 but America's entry into the war upset negotiations.

During the war, demands for power became so urgent that the two governments came close to starting work on the power project. But Congress, because of the power-

32

ful influence of the railroads, coal-mining industry, and U.S. port and shipping interests, always threw the seaway idea out. In every succeeding session of Congress from 1944 to 1954, a new bill in slightly modified form demanding early construction of the seaway was introduced —but never approved. Every president from Hoover onwards strongly favoured the seaway. President Truman told the Canadian Parliament in June, 1947, that the U.S. and Canada *must* develop it together. Eisenhower was enthusiastic about it. But Congress was adamant.

In 1948, Ontario Hydro and the N.Y. Power Authority tried to by-pass the two Federal Governments to get work started. They thought they might get the International Joint Commission to authorize the entire power project. It was a daring idea, but it did not work. The Canadian Government refused to permit the application to be made. In a letter to Robert Saunders, Secretary of State for External Affairs, Lester B. Pearson wrote:

"The Government considers that your application should not be filed with the International Joint Commission until the intentions of the U.S. Government have been ascertained. This decision results from Canada's commitments under the Great Lakes-St. Lawrence Basin Agreement of 1941. We do not wish to take the initiative in a course of action which might have the effect of nullifying an international agreement without knowing that the U.S. Government had decided upon a similar course. The Government has already started consultations with the U.S. authorities."

The demand for power kept growing. Prime Minister St. Laurent personally sought American co-operation in a visit to President Truman at the beginning of 1949, without success. In the meantime, the two Power Authorities waited with increasing restiveness for action. One high Hydro official once said to me, "Talk about water, water everywhere and not a drop to drink! If we soon don't get permission to go ahead with hydro power on the St. Lawrence, we'll have to begin building steam

33

generating plants. I can't imagine anything more ridiculous with all that water power going to waste."

The vast basin of the St. Lawrence is one of the great reservoirs of "white power" in the world. Although we do not fully know the potential of this area yet, it is probably between 25 million and 30 million horsepower. It is interesting to compare this with "black power"— coal. Assuming that one pound of coal would produce one kilowatt hour of electrical energy, it would take about 57 million tons of coal consumed annually to produce 25 million horsepower. Coal is an exhaustible asset; once burned it is gone for ever. But white power, after development, is inexhaustible.

The white power assets of the St. Lawrence region are divided in two. First are the rivers and streams which flow from the rim of the basin into the Great Lakes and the St. Lawrence River. Second are the Great Lakes connecting channels and the St. Lawrence itself. Hydroelectric power is nothing more than rain and snow on its way to the sea via rivers and streams. During the last ninety years, an average of thirty-two inches of rain and snow has fallen annually in this St. Lawrence area.

To get the full benefit from the power potential resulting from the 32 inches of annual precipitation on the St. Lawrence watershed, it is necessary to institute the construction of a comprehensive series of storage dams which would impound the rainfall, reduce the annual floods and control the flow of streams draining the watershed, such as the Ottawa, St. Maurice, Saguenay, Bersimis and Manicouagan. These would collect and store waters during periods of heavy rain and produce a dependable flow of water.

A great deal of the 25 million horsepower I have mentioned has already been developed. Hydro-electric in-

34

White Power

stallations along the Ottawa River, for instance, totalled about 2,500,000 horsepower by the end of 1956. The St. Maurice River, by 1956, had developed about 1,600,000 horsepower, and the Saguenay, Lake St. John and Peribonka River had developed nearly 3,000,000 horsepower. Lastly, the Manicouagan watershed is faced with development. It may eventually produce more than four million horsepower. A number of other rivers which have substantial resources have not been appraised yet.

On the St. Lawrence, from Superior to the sea, the hydro-electric potential is measured by a fall of 582 feet and an average flow of between 70,000 to 250,000 cubic feet per second. The first fall is between Lake Superior and Lake Huron, where St. Mary's River runs over St. Mary's Falls in a drop of twenty-two feet. Potential power here, as yet undeveloped, is 185,000 horsepower. Next, between Lake Huron and Lake Erie, the water drops eight feet in nearly ninety miles, too little to develop power economically.

The third step is between Lake Erie and Lake Ontario where the river plunges down 326 feet. If we could harness all this energy, we would have about 7 million horsepower. But to do so would mean destroying Niagara Falls. So great has been the demand for hydro power in Ontario and New York that Canada and the U.S. signed a treaty in 1950 governing the use of power at Niagara Falls and guaranteeing that power demands will never diminish the flow over the falls beyond an agreed amount. Even with these restrictions, however, a considerable potential is usable—from a maximum of three and a half million horsepower to a minimum of one and three-quarters of a million, depending on the flow of water in different seasons.

The fourth step down the river is between Lake Ontario and Lake St. Francis, which includes the International Rapids. The total fall is more than 90 feet. This is the vital section where Ontario and New York wanted to build power-houses and co-operatively generate the

35

maximum available horsepower—2.2 million. The fifth step is between Lake St. Francis and Lake St. Louis where there is a drop of a little more than 80 feet. Potential horsepower here is close to 2 million. The great Beauharnois Light, Heat and Power Company powerhouse had already developed about three-quarters of this before seaway work started. As we began building the seaway, Quebec Hydro extended the power-house by another 500,000 horsepower and so used the last of the potential power.

The sixth and last step in this water-fall to the sea is between Lake St. Louis and Montreal Harbour. The river here is supplemented by a portion of the flow from the Ottawa River which divides and flows around the island of Montreal. The fall is close to fifty feet, mainly down the Lachine Rapids, and the potential power is about 1,200,000 horsepower, all of it undeveloped.

When the last of the power is developed in the International Rapids, Ontario will be left with practically no more hydro-electric power. Quebec will still have plenty of potential. But Ontario may be saved from more expensive power by the harnessing of nuclear energy. Recent developments suggest that nuclear power may be able to compete with coal power within twenty years.

To develop the power of the river, co-operation was needed between the Federal Government, Ontario, Quebec, the State of New York and the U.S. Government. Each party had interests to protect and each had to make compromises. When we met the Ontario delegation in the Prime Minister's office—where Robert Saunders made his offer—the waters of Lake Ontario were then in a high-water cycle. The residents of the south shore were complaining that this was caused by an earth and rock fill which Canada had built across part of the river near Prescott about fifty years earlier.

This dam, the Gut, had been the centre of a bitter controversy and was blamed for the damage caused to these riparian owners. The Canadian Government was faced

36

at the time of the meeting with huge claims for property damage. We had agreed to remove the dam, even though engineering reports clearly indicated that it was not responsible for the flooding. We found that the Ontario delegation was concerned about the province's liability.

Premier Frost said he feared what might happen should anything go wrong during construction. He felt that by developing power resources on the International Rapids, the government could easily lay itself open to claims by Lake Ontario residents, whether the power development was responsible or not.

The Prime Minister emphasized that we did not think damage claims were likely. But we could not convince our listeners. So we inserted a clause into the agreement which, while making the Ontario Government responsible for damage claims arising out of the construction of the power works, absolved it of some other responsibilities. We decided that if damage claims came from any point up the river from Spencer Island, which is near Prescott (and therefore many miles upriver from the area which might possibly be affected by power development) the Government of Ontario would not be responsible.

Later we removed the Gut Dam, but it did not lower the level of Lake Ontario. None of the damage claims against us were proceeded with in the courts. The Prime Minister emphasized to Premier Frost that the agreement would be signed in the expectation that the U.S. would not participate. "We may," he said, "have to build the canal before the power project but of course we are not anxious to do this."

Ontario was always most anxious to develop the hydro-electric power resources along its section of the river. But Quebec was not. It had plenty of hydro power. Any joint arrangement to develop power and navigation, the Quebec Government felt, would be a sacrifice of provincial rights. Premier Duplessis was prepared to pay an extremely high price to preserve them.

It is often surprising for visitors to Montreal, who have

37

knowledge of hydro power, to notice the great Lachine Rapids tumbling down into the harbour, but with no hydro-electric power-house anywhere along their length. "Quebec must have enormous quantities of cheap power," it has been said, "to be able to ignore this power potential at the gates of Montreal."

As Minister of Transport, I had appointed a board of engineers in 1947, headed by a well known consulting engineer, Mr. R. A. C. Henry, to study how the potential power at Lachine might best be developed in conjunction with the building of a seaway channel. The board discussed the matter extensively with Quebec Hydro and ultimately chose two plans of development which had been worked out in co-operation with Quebec Hydro engineers. These plans were submitted to us for consideration.

We found that by combining construction of the seaway channel with the construction of a power-house at Victoria Bridge, the province could be saved spending about $25 million. So I made an appointment with Premier Duplessis to explain what we had been doing and how we might co-operate in the future.

But he said he would not commit himself to any agreement for joint development of power and navigation in the Lachine section. "I will not go along with you, but neither will I obstruct you," he said. I pointed out that the co-operative power-navigation plan had the approval of Quebec Hydro and would save millions of dollars for the province, but he remained unmoved. I discussed this with Premier Duplessis on a number of other occasions but we never made any headway. He emphasized that his lack of co-operation was not a personal matter, but as a representative of the Federal Government, I could not expect his help.

He did not like the Prime Minister and said so. Premier Duplessis never actually hindered our efforts to get the seaway built. He was content to remain a passive bystander of the great project.

38

White Power

By 1950, Ontario Hydro and the N.Y. State Power Authority had agreed how they would develop the power on the St. Lawrence. They decided to build jointly one great power-house, 3,300 feet long, about two miles west of Cornwall. The power-house would back up the river for 28 miles, creating a 100-square-mile lake. Buried under the waters would be the remains of more than 225 farms, half a dozen villages and towns, 18 cemeteries, 35 miles of highway, 40 miles of double-track railway. Six thousand five hundred people would lose their homes and property.

They planned to build two dams. One, the Long Sault, would control the water flow to the power-house and would be 2,250 feet long and nearly 150 feet high. The second, the Iroquois, would be 2,450 feet long and would control the outflow from Lake Ontario.

The two power agencies would pay $650,000,000 for this work and would remove 95 million cubic yards of earth and rock. They would use about seven million tons of concrete, sand and stone for the construction.

These figures show how urgently the two Power Authorities wanted power from the river. If the St. Lawrence Seaway Authority had been forced to cause similar disruption to residents by the river, the seaway might have been delayed longer than it was. But the Power Authorities could prove their case. They were desperate for power.

The completion of the co-operative plans for the development of power between Cornwall and Iroquois was the close of an epoch in the events leading up to the seaway. The power people now waited for the rest of us to move. The two governments could look back on a score of opportunities to build which had been lost. In the twenties, we had been too busy or too worried about our war debt to get construction going. During the thirties, we had been obsessed by economic problems, and too

39

worried about the implications of the seaway, to begin construction. During the early part of the war, we had been close to justifying an immediate start, but then had decided that offence was more important than defence and our money and efforts had gone to guns and bullets rather than canals and power-generating stations. Post-war, we had frittered the time away with little progress.

It was discouraging, at this time, to look retrospectively at the seaway and power project idea. Wooten and Bowden had completed their report thirty years before and this had failed to get action. The countless other reports, collectively running to many millions of words, were gathering dust on government shelves in two countries.

I remember finding a report published in 1943 by a Toronto engineer, Norman D. Wilson, in the library of the Department of Transport. Wilson had been retained by the Federal Government after the 1941 Great Lakes waterway agreement, to examine how the flooding of the International Rapids section, necessary to develop the power there, would affect the surrounding countryside. Wilson's report, like that of Bowden and Wooten, reflected his great enthusiasm for the project.

He reported how the people living by the river would be affected, where new town-sites should be established, how the historic monuments and houses should be preserved, what we should do with the great United Empire Loyalist cemeteries. He suggested a giant causeway linking high points of land near the river which would emerge as islands after flooding. He urged the creation of a great parkland area. Much of his report was put into action later by the Ontario Government.

After reading the report, I recalled all the other men who had been similarly enthusiastic about the seaway idea. Enthusiasm, treaties, hard work and idealism were apparently not enough. I wondered what would be necessary to get the seaway started.

40

CHAPTER FOUR

THE ALL-CANADIAN SEAWAY

Seizing the Initiative

The U.S. Comes In

Work Begins

SEIZING THE INITIATIVE

It was always possible for Canada to ignore the United States and build the seaway alone. But it was not practicable before 1930. Canada was not then a wealthy country and was hampered by its war debt. It was not feasible after 1930 because of the depression. It was impossible during the war. But by 1950, our impatience at the delaying tactics of American business interests and the U.S. Congress had prepared us to tell the United States what should be done. Canada had discovered that it was rich with oil and minerals. Its wealth gave it power and confidence disproportionate to its small population.

Prime Minister St. Laurent and I were discussing the thirty years of delay to the seaway one evening in Ottawa in 1950 when he said, "We should build the seaway alone. I think the Americans should be made aware of our determination to get the seaway built." As Canadians, we were unanimous that the seaway must be built. If we determined to go ahead alone, the U.S. might be stirred into action.

The "Canadian Seaway" idea quickly went beyond the conversation stage. The Prime Minister suggested that I assume responsibility for spreading the idea of the all-Canadian seaway. It would be my task to get public opinion, and particularly that in the U.S., accustomed to the idea of Canada going ahead alone if necessary.

Of course, if Canada did go ahead alone, power could still be developed in the International Rapids section. That would have to be a joint development between Ontario Hydro and the Power Authority of New York, with the approval of both governments. But this did not worry us. It was more important to get some action.

The first time I publicly mentioned the concept of the all-Canadian seaway was at the Warden's Banquet, held at Cornwall on September 14, 1950. I can recall snatches from that speech, how there "must be no more delay . . .

43

we must unbottle the lake carriers . . . urgent that we develop the water power." The crux of the speech was, "If Congress does not want to take action, we should begin making plans to go ahead alone."

After the speech, I was immediately approached by the two reporters from the Cornwall, Ontario, and Massena, New York, newspapers. "Does this statement have the approval of the government?" I was asked. I said it was a personal opinion, but that it was widely shared. "Do you think that an all-Canadian seaway is possible?" was another question. I said it certainly was possible and if Congress did not act soon, it would become a fact.

However, my statement did not have quite the impact that was intended. I learned later that many people felt that I was just trying to draw attention to the seaway problem by making a statement that was sure to get headlines. Of course, the history of the seaway is filled with ill-informed and inaccurate statements by all kinds of public figures. However, Lester Pearson, C. D. Howe and Prime Minister St. Laurent all supported the all-Canadian seaway concept in statements of their own. Their views were widely applauded in Canada and secured some attention in the U.S., but many people doubted that Canada seriously intended to construct the seaway alone.

This was not to imply that all the interest in the seaway was confined to Canada. Although many American commercial interests were bitterly opposed to the seaway, most American Government officials were enthusiastically in favour of it. I remember chatting with a congressman one time who said he was ashamed to look at Congress's record in stalling the seaway. "There are far more representatives in Congress who are for the seaway than against it," he said, "but you have tremendously powerful business interests against you. They control a lot of votes."

On another occasion, I was attending a banquet at Cornwall at which a U.S. congressman had been invited

44

The All-Canadian Seaway

to speak briefly on the seaway, following a visit of a Congressional Committee to the site of the future power works. To our surprise, once he began speaking, nothing could stop him. He became quite impassioned about the seaway and fiercely decried the efforts that had been made to stop the development of the enterprise.

At one point in his speech with which I was in hearty agreement I said "Hear, hear!" To my surprise and embarrassment, he turned and looked angrily at me. Obviously he had misunderstood the meaning of my words and thought I was rudely interrupting. Men like this, who believed in the seaway with utter conviction, came from both sides of the border.

The American enthusiasm for the seaway in face of their country's repeated rejection of the project always seemed contradictory to Canadians. I remember one time when Secretary of State for External Affairs Lester Pearson and I went to Washington to ask President Truman for U.S. support for the power project portion of the seaway, we were besieged by reporters after the meeting at the White House. For Pearson, this was routine, but for myself it was extremely confusing. Questions were fired at us so quickly that I could hardly follow them. "What does this meeting mean?" "Are you going ahead without us?" "Can you handle seaway construction on your own?" and so on.

Despite congressional vetoes, the seaway was always vitally interesting to Americans generally. It was particularly significant to nearly sixty million Americans living in eight states adjoining the Great Lakes.

I spent the winter of 1950-1 re-emphasizing the feasibility of an all-Canadian seaway in speeches and in private discussions. Although I was cast in a role resembling that of a one-man promotion campaign, I did not feel as though I was successfully shaping public opinion. In fact, though there was interest and support for our proposals, I felt that my listeners did not really believe that Canada could build the seaway alone.

45

However, by the fall of 1951, the government was ready to act. The Prime Minister formally presented the Canadian seaway idea to the cabinet, which unanimously approved and decided that Prime Minister St. Laurent should go to Washington and outline to President Truman the work we had already done. He should ask for formal presidential support for the Power Authority to build its share of the power works.

When Mr. St. Laurent told President Truman officially that we were going ahead with the work, the surprise in Washington was complete. "Canada will go seaway alone" said the headlines, and the newspapers and radio broadcasts were full of conjecture as to what effect our actions would have. President Truman said he would support the Canadian action but only as a second best if Congress became deadlocked again. "I strongly believe we should make this a joint development," he told Prime Minister St. Laurent. It was amusing to us to see the almost shocked U.S. reaction to our proposals after we had spent many months trying to warn them about our intentions.

Although Canada appreciated President Truman's conditional support, it made little difference to the outcome. We were committed to going ahead. The only unknown quantity was whether we could persuade the U.S. to cooperate. After Prime Minister St. Laurent's meeting with President Truman, there were long discussions in Ottawa at cabinet level—which, of course, I am not permitted to reveal—resulting in a decision on how we would go ahead alone.

Our plan took two directions. First, we instructed government lawyers to draw up "an act respecting the Construction of Works for the Generation of Electric Power in the International Rapids Section of the St. Lawrence River". This act was based on the agreement that Prime Minister St. Laurent and I had signed with Premier Frost of Ontario and George Challies in 1951. The Act gave Ontario Hydro authority to construct works for the

46

generation of power in the International Section of the river. The second bill was the St. Lawrence Seaway Authority Act.

As a result of our experiences during the war, we knew that the most effective method of getting government work done was to establish a Crown company and give it enough authority to do the work. The Seaway Authority needed two powers. It must be able to expropriate land. It must be able to dig a channel and build locks.

I introduced both bills in the House of Commons on December 4, 1951. C. D. Howe, who had signed the 1941 agreement on behalf of Canada and whose interest in the seaway had been intense for many years, sat with me during the discussion. The House was full and there was deep attention during the debate. I explained how Ontario would develop more than one-million horsepower near Cornwall, how Lachine could be developed at any time. I emphasized the economic effect of the seaway, how it would spur the development of Labrador and northern Quebec iron ore mines, how it would cut the cost of the prairie grain. I knew, as I looked around the House while speaking, that there would be unanimous approval of both bills. The day before, a Maritime member had come to me and said, "I'm not going to oppose the bill but I think it's going to work against our coal industry." I said that it would reduce the price of other materials. "Yes," he said, "but coal is the only really important item to us." But he was willing to support the seaway bill. Support would be unanimous because everybody in the House recognized that if it was beneficial to the whole nation, it would be ultimately beneficial to separate parts of Canada. There was some partisanship in the House about the seaway. To many men, going ahead with the seaway was notice to the U.S. that we were now a first-class power. Some of my colleagues felt it was high time the U.S. was made aware of this.

The House support *was* unanimous. In a rare moment, the three Opposition leaders in the House—George A.

47

Drew (Progressive Conservative), M. J. Coldwell (Co-operative Commonwealth Federation), and J. H. Blackmore (Social Credit)—enthusiastically supported the bills.

Later, when members were informally congratulating me, one member said, "I wouldn't have supported the bill because I don't think it's got anything to do with my constituency. But I would like to see the U.S. being shoved out of the limelight." Another member from the prairies said he felt that the probable benefits to his area had been over-emphasized but he was keen to see an all-Canadian seaway. "In fact," he said, "I hope you can prevent the Americans getting their hands on the seaway at all. I would rather we sacrificed our chance at hydro power on the river to keep the seaway all-Canadian."

Immediately after the bills had been passed, before they received Royal Assent by the Governor General on December 21, 1951, and January 11, 1952, I was flooded with requests to speak all over the country on the seaway. For a time, I could have spoken three or four times a week. Later, I even received invitations to address shipping interests in Italy and to attend the Baltic and International Maritime Conference in Copenhagen, Denmark. Subsequently, I flew to Copenhagen, addressed the conference and found great European interest in the seaway. At that time, the Europeans were angry at the United States for stipulating that all Marshall Aid must be carried by U.S. ships. They felt, by contrast, that Canada's seaway represented more European opportunity, not less. I found later that even while German, Dutch and Scandinavian ship-owners were querying me about ship sizes for the waterway, they were already planning construction of new ships which would be able to use the seaway with the maximum efficiency.

It was now the spring of 1952. We knew that we must keep the seaway idea moving. The Secretary of State for External Affairs Lester Pearson and I visited President Truman in the spring, and as a result he sent letters

48

to the U.S. Senate and House of Representatives Committees.

He said, "The question before the Congress now is not whether the seaway should be built but whether the United States should share in its construction, operation and control. The Canadian Government is ready and willing to build a deep seaway from Montreal to Lake Erie on the Canadian side of the boundary, if Congress does not authorize the United States Government to participate in building the joint Canadian-United States Seaway agreed to in 1941.

"In order to lose no time if the Congress does not act, however, we have agreed at a recent meeting that the application to the International Joint Commission will be completed and filed at an early date. Thus the arrangements are nearly completed for proceeding with the St. Lawrence project by an alternative means if this Congress fails to ratify the 1941 Agreement."

Truman's appeal had no immediate effect. But in the fall, a presidential election brought Dwight D. Eisenhower into power. Throughout his campaign, he had supported the St. Lawrence Seaway so we had no doubts about his feelings. In January, 1953, we learned at Ottawa that the Americans were preparing seaway legislation at last. President Eisenhower, we learned, had sent an urgent message to Congress saying that if Congress acted quickly, Canada might still agree to a joint development of the seaway.

At the same time, the U.S. ambassador at Ottawa called on Prime Minister St. Laurent to say that his country hoped Canada would leave the door open for the U.S. on the project. The Prime Minister decided that Canada's reply must clearly show that we would tolerate no more delays, no matter how well intentioned the Americans might be. He wrote to the Ambassador and said his government would be reluctant to start any discussions which would delay the seaway. About this time, Congressman Dondero and Senator Alexander Wiley intro-

49

duced seaway bills, later to be called the Wiley-Dondero Act, to their respective houses.

We had lost our opportunity because of this flurry of American activity to begin construction during the 1953 season. But we were satisfied to be making the best progress at any time since the idea of building the seaway was first mentioned. Lester B. Pearson pleaded with Mr. Dulles to name the American power entity so that we could at least get to work in 1954.

THE U.S. COMES IN

Through the fall of 1953, events kept moving. President Eisenhower signed an executive order designating the Power Authority of the State of New York as the entity to develop the U.S. share of the power on the St. Lawrence. He also appointed United States members to the Joint Board of Engineers, the international body which was supposed to oversee the construction of the seaway. A week later, R. A. C. Henry and myself were named Canadian members. In December, the Federal Power Commission licensed the N.Y. State Power Authority to develop the U.S. share of power. There were numerous appeals against this licence by private power companies. As we watched and waited impatiently, the appeals were dismissed one by one during 1954. On May 13 President Eisenhower signed the Wiley-Dondero Act, and on June 7 the U.S. Supreme Court dismissed the last of the power appeals.

At first, when the news reached Ottawa, there was much disappointment. The idea of Canada building the seaway alone was immensely popular. There was some resentment that the Americans were belatedly jumping aboard. But this feeling soon passed. It was realized that U.S. co-operation was diplomatically and practically the best thing. The seaway would be paid for largely by American ships. It was preferable that the U.S. have a

50

voice in the construction of the project.

As soon as the St. Lawrence Seaway Authority was first mentioned in the bill I introduced at the end of 1951, there was almost constant speculation by newspapers and others as to who would head the Authority. I seemed to be the favoured choice, largely because of my close association with the St. Lawrence. During 1954, the rumours became strong that I was to be president of the Authority.

When I was discussing in the House my estimates for the Department of Transport in 1954, while we were waiting for U.S. action, several members interrupted me. "I realize," said one, "that the honourable member is giving us these figures for the last time and that he is undoubtedly very busy with other affairs."

These "other affairs" were news to me. But at the beginning of June I was unofficially told at a high level that if I wanted to take the presidency of the Seaway Authority the job was mine.

It was a difficult moment. I had been a member of the House constantly since October, 1935, when I was elected Liberal member for Stormont. Although my interest in the seaway was always intense, it was pure coincidence that I happened to be Minister of Transport and to introduce the bills necessary to get it started. I had been a member of the cabinet for nine years, and although some of the glamour of that had worn off, I was not anxious to quit my political career.

I felt, in pessimistic moments, that by taking the presidency, I would be submerging myself in a political backwater. Balancing this was the thought that here was an opportunity to help with one of the most exciting construction projects ever undertaken in the history of the world. Eventually, I spoke to the Prime Minister. While he made it clear that the decision should be mine, I sensed his feelings. I felt sure he thought I should take it. "I think it is a great opportunity," he said. "We will miss you in the House."

Towards the end of June, I decided I would take the

51

job. The Wiley-Dondero Bill had passed through the House of Representatives and it looked as though we would be working with the U.S. But before I accepted the position, I was mentally choosing the men to get the seaway started. The job would be insupportable without the right type of executive help.

Between 1943 and 1945, I was C. D. Howe's parliamentary assistant in the Department of Munitions and Supply. During that time I met a young lawyer named Charles Gavsie from the Department of Munitions and Supply. At one time during the war when we were negotiating an important contract with the U.S. Navy, Howe sent me to Washington with Gavsie. I was highly impressed by his understanding and handling of financial matters. In his personal dealings with the Americans, he displayed a sureness and confidence which I did not forget. Subsequently, he became deputy minister of National Revenue, Taxation Division. Because the seaway would be dealing with millions of dollars, involved in dozens of complicated construction contracts, I needed a financial expert and I hoped Gavsie would be the man.

It was no less important that I get first-class engineers to help me, preferably men who had experience with canals or maritime work of some kind. The choice was not difficult. I had met C. W. West some years previously when he was chief engineer of the Welland Canal, and knew he would make an excellent member of the seaway executive. The then manager of the Port of Montreal, Gordon Murphy, was another man I wanted. He had a reputation for getting things done, a particular talent for unusual solutions to difficult problems. I was thankful that I had sent R. A. C. Henry to Montreal to get his special projects branch of the Department of Transport into operation. Henry was a distinguished public servant. He was a former deputy minister of Railways and Canals and chairman of the Air Transport Board. The branch was making great progress, and had surveyed most of the river and all the Lachine section at Montreal. One of

52

the first things I would do, I decided, would be to incorporate this branch into the Seaway Authority.

Not only did I need men of technical skill. They must also be men of personal charm and diplomacy. It was not hard to foresee the opportunities in the future for personality clashes, particularly if the seaway became an international project. The seaway could be hamstrung by petty bickering in committees.

At the end of the previous year, with R. A. C. Henry, I had been appointed to the St. Lawrence Joint Board of Engineers, which theoretically was created to supervise the construction work of the seaway even though it was then a long way from beginning. This board consisted of three Canadians and three Americans. I could see, at one or two of the meetings, that there would be many opportunities for international squabbling. And there were many other boards which would be helping to build the seaway.

There was the St. Lawrence Board of Control which had no jurisdiction over the construction but which would come into full operation when construction was finished. It had certain advisory functions during construction but its real duties began after completion of the power works and related to water levels and regulation of the discharge of water from Lake Ontario and the flow of the water in the International Rapids section. These duties are all-important. Arising out of these duties a method of regulation has been in the process of development and there is now a dispute between the power entities and the two governments as to the responsibility of damages which may result from the inauguration of the method of control. There was the International Lake Level Board which was a purely temporary Board, appointed by the International Joint Commission in 1952 and which recommended a modified rule of regulation of Lake Ontario in 1956. This rule has been modified somewhat since, and I believe that in the near future the report of this Board will be completed and, its work having been

53

completed, the Board itself disbanded.

Finally, there was the International Joint Commission, which was ultimately responsible for everything, since it was not only an international administrative body but also a high court. The I.J.C. could, for instance, handle the complaints of any municipality which complained that seaway work was polluting its water supply. It could deal with the charges of any private citizen that changed water levels were damaging his property. The I.J.C. created the Joint Board of Engineers and the Lake Level Board. It recommended the creation of the International Board of Control.

The personal relations side of the seaway, I considered, was therefore very important. The Seaway Authority was lucky that all the men I have mentioned were keen to help build the project.

WORK BEGINS

One of the most impressive things about the seaway was the speed with which construction began. It was July 1 before I was formally appointed president, Gavsie vice-president and West the member of the committee to run the St. Lawrence Seaway Authority. We had no power before that. But by October, the first contract was awarded. After thirty years of delay, it seemed we were ready to make up for lost time. We were greatly helped now by the earlier days. It had given engineers, surveyors and draughtsmen enough time to prepare all the plans and specifications. The first contract we award-ed was for the construction of a channel and dyke be-tween the Victoria and Jacques Cartier Bridges in Mont-real Harbour. We were also able to report that work would start immediately on the construction of a canal and lock across Iroquois Point, near Iroquois, and to arrange for the expropriation of about 238 acres of land south of the existing Galops Canal; also to call tenders

54

for the $14,000,000 canal and lock at Iroquois on December 1, 1955. Perhaps it was fitting that the Power Authorities officially opened the seaway project. It had been power which had been responsible for much of our urgency in getting the seaway started. Both Ontario Hydro and the N.Y. Power Authority were ready to move on the day the final agreement was made.

At one point, a grand opening was planned. President Eisenhower was to be there. Many American officials wanted the opening to be colourful and spectacular. In Ottawa, we learned that tentative plans were being made in Washington for plane-loads of reporters, photographers, TV and radio commentators to be flown up for the opening. It became clear that the opening would cost the Authority tens of thousands of dollars. We would have no hope of matching the American preparations. Canada would be swamped in colourful opening fanfare. We did not think this was a suitable way to begin the seaway. As gracefully as possible we let the Americans know that we were not particularly anxious to be involved in a huge opening ceremony.

The Power Authorities, however, did not have the same reservations. Ontario Hydro, one of the largest electrical utilities in the world took the lion's share of representing Canada at the special opening ceremonies at Massena, New York, and Cornwall, Ontario, where the guest of honour list looked like an international Who's Who. There was Prime Minister Louis St. Laurent, Premier Leslie M. Frost of Ontario, Governor Thomas E. Dewey of the State of New York, Robert Saunders, chairman of the Ontario Hydro Electric Power Commission, Robert Moses, president of the Power Authority of the State of New York, the Rt. Honourable C. D. Howe, Minister of Trade and Commerce, the Hon. George Challies, and many others. Present also were the executive officers of the St. Lawrence Seaway Development Corporation, including the administrator Lewis G. Castle, later to become my friend and colleague.

55

Work Begins

It was a significant moment. Louis St. Laurent echoed the thoughts of many. "Rivers," he said, "together with mountains and deserts, have been long considered as natural barriers which make excellent national frontiers because they divide peoples from one another. While this may still be true to a certain extent, it is no longer the case as far as the St. Lawrence River is concerned. More and more, this great waterway has become a bond rather than a barrier between Americans and Canadians."

Even before the official ceremonies were over, arrangements were being made to send seaway construction trucks rolling along New York, Ontario and Quebec roads. They would carry bulldozers, cranes, drag-line equipment, explosives, cement, steel, shovels and men. Field offices would be hammered together all along the St. Lawrence. One of the greatest construction projects of all time was about to begin.

56

The All-Canadian Seaway

CHAPTER FIVE

CONSTRUCTION BEGINS

Working Together

On the Job

WORKING TOGETHER

Both Canada and the U.S. were determined, in the fall of 1954, to get the seaway built as quickly as possible. The first meeting with the St. Lawrence Seaway Development Corporation, headed by Lewis G. Castle, was a historic and somewhat humorous moment. The Americans arrived at the conference room with the agenda of the meeting prepared. One of my colleagues said to me just before the meeting started, "I presume we will table the agenda at the next meeting." I said nothing and decided not to mention the matter at that time.

At the next meeting, the agenda was carefully prepared for us again, packed with subjects that the Americans wanted to discuss. But there was nothing there from Canada. Some of my colleagues were angry. There was, almost before we had started, the makings of a first-class row. And yet nobody could be more co-operative or more genial in discussions than the Americans. Obviously, they had assumed we would be thankful they were handling this work.

Rather than risk heated words in the conference room, I called Castle and pointed out that we thought it might be more suitable if we prepared the agenda jointly. "There are," I said drily, "often some things we would like discussed, too." He agreed immediately.

It was typical of our American colleagues that once they began work, they felt they were invested with the responsibility of doing the whole job. Whether this was because they felt that nobody could do it as well as they, I don't know. We had to remind them politely from time to time that they were not building the Canadian section of the project.

An American administrative officer once suggested that the costs of some of our Montreal works should not be included in computing tolls. I replied by pointing out

59

that the operating costs of some of the American works were, in our opinion, far too high. It could be argued that the Americans should not be allowed to charge the full amount of all their works. In this situation lay possible trouble. Mutual ignorance, with both parties working away at their own projects, could quickly blow up into major disagreement. So in later discussions we agreed that each country would first of all determine what was a correct capital cost of works to be undertaken. Each country would let the other know what was being done and would make a full disclosure of all costs.

American ignorance of the Canadian point of view was at first serious. It extended to strange heights. At one of the meetings between the corporation and our authority, I suggested to Castle that he come and meet the Prime Minister, Mr. St. Laurent. He was delighted and we spent a pleasant half-hour discussing the seaway in the Prime Minister's office.

Later, when I was attending a similar meeting in Washington, D.C., Castle invited me to meet the President. President Eisenhower was extremely cordial and in the middle of our informal talk—during which we had discussed tentative plans for President Eisenhower's attendance at the official opening ceremony—he walked over to a large globe in the corner of his office and said, "You must show me, Chevrier, just where this place Massena is located."

I showed him the town, in northern New York State, just south of Cornwall, Ontario. Then he said, "You know, it seems ridiculous. We both speak the same language. We think alike. We behave the same. Don't you think you would be better off as the 49th state?"

For a moment, I was speechless. The remark was made lightly and I thought the President might be joking. I said formally, "I can assure you, sir, that nobody in any of our ten provinces has the slightest desire to be incorporated into the U.S.A." The conversation passed quickly on to other things, but I reflected that it would

60

be interesting to suggest to the President that the U.S. consider becoming Canada's eleventh province.

Many Americans working with us at the field level were surprised to find that we were constructing two-thirds of the seaway. Some were surprised to find our engineers just as competent as theirs. But these problems were petty ones—although I still have difficulty accepting the humour of the 49th state idea—and that was why I was so certain we must have tactful executives to deal with the Americans. This was no time for delays over small and unimportant quarrels.

Soon after the U.S. decided to join us in seaway construction, they met with us in July in the east block of the House of Commons at Ottawa. Representing the United States were the Secretary of Defense Robert B. Anderson, Wilbur Brucker, a counsel in the Department of Justice, who was later to become Secretary of the U.S. Army, Lewis G. Castle, the seaway development corporation administrator and his deputy administrator Martin W. Oettershagen. There were also representatives from the U.S. Corps of Engineers, the State Department, and a number of lawyers. On our side, there was Lester Pearson, the Secretary of State for External Affairs and his colleagues Max Wershof and Ernest Côté; Gavsie, West and myself of the Seaway Authority, and our own lawyers.

At this meeting the Americans quickly emphasized that their legislation directed them to build *all* the facilities in the International Rapids section in the United States territory. This was an early attempt by the U.S. to get sole control of the seaway along that section of the river. They did not want us to duplicate their facilities on our side of the river. This was serious for us. Naturally we wanted to leave the door open to build parallel Canadian canal facilities. We did not want the interests of another country to dominate a seaway that was seventy-five per cent Canadian. Pearson and our delegation discussed this problem intensively. We finally agreed on a

61

Working Together

solution. There was no point in fighting the U.S. point of view, and it was only a point of view at that early stage. Instead, we would counter by presenting our own case. It was decided that Pearson would make a public announcement that Canada would build a canal and a lock at Iroquois at the head of the International Rapids. This was in seeming contradiction to the Americans who had said they were going to do that work on their side of the river. As it happened, Canada went ahead with her plans immediately. The U.S. delayed taking action, probably because no U.S. plans had been made, and sufficient money had not been appropriated by Congress to do all the work. The result was that the U.S. eventually recognized the Iroquois lock and made no attempt to stop our work or complain about it.

At a later meeting, the Americans proposed that the seaway should be dredged south of Cornwall Island, at the foot of the International Rapids, and thence upstream through American territory. We did not argue with this.

But in diverting the channel south of Cornwall Island, Cornwall was being deprived of deep-water facilities. "This city prospered because of navigation," I told the meeting, "first with nine-foot draught canals, later with 14-foot canals. The city has a vested right to 27-foot facilities at its front door."

This situation again reflected the American fear that if they left us an opportunity to build a duplicate seaway on our side of the river, they would eventually lose all control of the project. Such a loss would be against their policies. It was, for their defence experts, tactically unacceptable to permit such a valuable waterway running along a border to be entirely in the hands of a "foreign" power, regardless of how friendly the U.S. might be with such a country.

From an economic point of view, the U.S. did not want to be deprived of all authority on a project to which her merchant marine would be contributing heavily in tolls. But what the Americans were proposing was most dam-

62

Construction Begins

aging to my home city of Cornwall. It would leave such big industries as Howard Smith Paper Mills Ltd., Canadian Cottons Ltd. and others without access to deepwater facilities. There would be little incentive for other industries to establish themselves on the outmoded canal and dock facilities. As a result of American efforts to forestall these, we were forced to emphasize publicly that "when traffic warranted it, we would build duplicate facilities on our side of the river". We did more than make a statement. We did the dredging on the Canadian side right up to the dyke where we inserted a structure capable of providing 27-foot navigation. We hoped when the time came that we would build a canal at Cornwall and that the United States would build duplicate facilities at Point Rockway, N.Y. opposite Iroquois, Ont.

ON THE JOB

After we, the Canadian Authority, had established ourselves in Ottawa with offices, we quickly settled to a routine of operation. The Special Projects branch of the Department of Transport, led by R. A. C. Henry, was working in Montreal, so we took over their offices (in fact, we took over the entire hydraulics division of the department), thus establishing secondary headquarters there.

At least once a week, we all met in the Ottawa board offices. On Mondays and Tuesdays, we dealt with administrative work in the capital. On Thursdays and Fridays, Gavsie, West and I worked in Montreal. This left Wednesday for field trips to keep us in touch with the physical progress of the work. There were many meetings with public bodies, municipalities, with engineers working on site, contractors and Quebec Government officials. Frequently, meetings that we had been holding during the day would continue on the train or plane, to Montreal, Washington, Toronto, Ottawa or New

63

York. All these meetings were interspersed about every three months with agency meetings between the Authority and the Development Corporation in Washington, Ottawa and New York.

We worked extremely hard. I thought perhaps the pressure of political life might be decreased a little in such a position. The reverse was true. One of our first problems was to decide on a location for a permanent headquarters and administration building for the Authority. Soon after we began work, the government decided that Cornwall should be the headquarters. By October, we had bought a site and made arrangements for a permanent headquarters building to be erected at Cornwall.

This was a wise choice and one that, needless to say, made me extremely pleased. Cornwall is in the heart of the International Section of the seaway development. It was then the headquarters of the Ontario-St. Lawrence Canals. After the opening of the seaway it became the administration headquarters of all canal services in Canada. Cornwall is situated almost midway between the Iroquois lock in the west and the Lachine section locks at Montreal in the east. More important, the United States Seaway Development Corporation had made its headquarters at Massena, N.Y., opposite Cornwall.

It was now late fall, and there was little time to get much construction work done before winter set in. However, I was determined to get some work going. We called for tenders for work at Iroquois and Montreal. I decided we would concentrate on Iroquois, push ahead as quickly as possible there and learn what problems faced us. Before the winter began, we had established field offices there and had begun hiring engineers for supervisory work on site.

It was becoming momentarily more clear that the entire construction project was going to be done at emergency speed. The Power Authorities said they wanted to begin generating power by 1958. This meant we had

64

Construction Begins

to construct the navigation works in four years. Most plans for construction of the navigation channel stipulated five years for building. This meant that contracts would have to be let quickly. Contractors would probably have to work three shifts a day. There might not always be enough time to check thoroughly the working records of the dozens of contractors involved. I remember how one "unknown" contractor successfully bid for a particularly difficult and expensive piece of construction. We had very grave doubts about his ability to do the work. To our surprise, he became one of the best contractors we had. Not only did he do the work with immaculate precision, but he finished well ahead of schedule. On another less memorable occasion, a very experienced contractor was replaced.

Before we could begin construction, however, we had to dispose of many problems. The first of these was the puzzle of the bridges. Between Montreal and Cornwall, seven bridges cross the seaway. Before the seaway was opened lakers and canallers were built to fit the locks and incidental structures along the canals. But the seaway had to fit lakers up to 25,000 tons in size and ocean vessels up to 9,000 tons. This meant that to conform to international navigation regulations, we had to give these ships at least 120 feet of clearance from the water to masthead level. But the very first bridge confronting the incoming ships to the seaway—the Jacques Cartier—allowed just sixty feet from water to bridge.

This long low bridge, a familiar sight to any visitor to Montreal, Longueuil and other south shore municipalities, had been one of the most heavily travelled bridges across the river for the last thirty odd years. So heavy was the traffic when seaway planners began surveying the bridge problem they found it would be impossible to interrupt traffic on this bridge for more than a few hours. Yet somehow an extra sixty feet of clearance had to be built into that bridge; nor could it be done by installing a vertical lift span, which consists of a movable section

65

of the bridge that can be raised rapidly but which cuts off traffic in the raised position.

The bridge was owned by the National Harbours Board, a federal agency, which was only too anxious to help us to modify the bridge to suit our purposes. But the roads leading to the bridge were administered by the provincial highways department and we were not sure of the department's co-operation. The engineers and designers of the bridge, Dominion Bridge Ltd., ultimately worked out an ingenious method of raising the bridge fifty feet without interrupting traffic. But it was going to be an expensive operation. I took the plan to Premier Duplessis and proposed to him that while we would pay for the alteration of the bridge itself, his highways department should build the new approaches for it. I left the plan with him to consider.

A few days later at a press conference he attacked the plan, as well as another plan which we had for the Victoria Bridge, particularly the suggestion that his highways department should be required to pay anything for construction. I made several more attempts to get agreement without success. So we made plans to go ahead alone. We planned to use fill we would be digging out of the seaway channel to pile up the high approaches to the bridge. The National Harbours Board would build the road on the fill and pave it. It would also build the piers. The Quebec department of highways would provide "consultative help".

Throughout the construction of the seaway, I tried to enlist as much co-operation and financial help as possible from other agencies. The charter of the Authority was specific: we were empowered merely to acquire land and build a channel and locks. Literally interpreted, this meant we could have installed a vertical lift span in the Jacques Cartier Bridge. This would have caused almost uncontrollable traffic jams throughout down-town Montreal. Clearly, this was impossible. Therefore, when we encountered such situations, we did whatever was most

66

Construction Begins

helpful to the people vitally affected. In return, we expected as much help and financial co-operation as possible. The Jacques Cartier Bridge project cost the Authority and the National Harbours Board $10 million.

The next bridge up the river, the Victoria, presented very different problems. It was a much older structure, and from the time it was built in 1898, it had two rail tracks and a sixteen-foot roadway. While the seaway was being built, one of the rail tracks was abandoned and a roadway was laid over it, thereby doubling the vehicular capacity of the bridge.

There was no hope of raising this bridge high enough to give ships clearance because of the rail tracks. It was a low-level bridge. The gradient would have been too steep for trains. The only alternative was to install a vertical lift span. But the problem with this was the same as at the Jacques Cartier. Rail and road traffic was so heavy that even a day's delay would cause chaos. Over a hundred trains a day crossed this bridge. When this figure was put against the estimated number of ships that would pass up and down the St. Lawrence in the same time—as many as thirty a day—it seemed to create a perfect impasse.

"What we need," said one engineer, "is a bridge with a lift span that raises and lowers itself 60 feet in 5 seconds allowing a ship to steam underneath at 50 knots. We need train drivers with nerves of steel who can judge to a split second when the span is going to be down."

It was our responsibility not to interrupt traffic. Our statute implied we must leave the bridges as nearly as possible as we found them. But this was impossible with the old Victoria. Numerous complaints had been made in Montreal about its dilapidated condition. Gavsie and I thought it best if we had an informal chat with Donald Gordon, the president of the Canadian National Railways, which owned the bridge, to see whether we could reach a friendly agreement. We arranged to see Gordon during our next regular visit to Montreal.

67

To our surprise, it soon became clear that this was going to be anything but an informal talk. Gordon was flanked by Starr Fairweather, chief of the C.N.R. Research and Development Branch, and Norman MacMillan, the C.N.R.'s legal adviser. The atmosphere in the office was formal, almost chilly. After some discussion unmarked by any spirit of compromise, I was forced to point out that the rights of navigation took priority over those of rail traffic.

At that, Gordon exploded angrily, "I'll be damned if anybody is going to tell me that a canal has got priority over a railway!" I said the seaway would install a vertical lift section in the bridge and build the approaches, but that was all we were prepared to do. Gordon vigorously disputed this. He said that a vertical lift would be impossible for a hundred train crossings a day to be maintained.

The discussion quickly reached a point where both of us obdurately refused to concede anything. Eventually, I said that our only course of action was to take our disagreement to the Minister of Transport himself. To this, Gordon agreed.

After Gavsie and I left the office, I realized that Gordon's attitude was justifiable as long as he believed the rights of the railway were inviolable. For him to concede that the seaway had prior rights would be an admission of its greater importance. No president of a billion-dollar business which would be in direct competition with the seaway would be likely to admit that.

Subsequently, we met in the office of the Minister of Transport, George Marler, and our disagreement quickly reached a point where I told Gordon exactly what I thought of the C.N.R. attitude. His obstinacy annoyed me because I could not see how the problem of the Victoria could be permitted to delay the seaway. The bridge was only one small obstacle in our path up the river. If it were going to take all this trouble to get past it, our progress up the river would be very slow indeed. After

68

Construction Begins

my outburst, I realized my mistake and formally apologized. Whether or not my apology mollified him, I don't know, but Gordon said, "Well, one thing is certain. You are not going to take any action on that bridge without paying me damages."

I said, "Of course, we will pay for the vertical lift span and the approaches."

Gordon said, "The vertical lift isn't good enough. It will delay my trains and jam up traffic for miles."

I pointed out that there was already a vertical lift span over the Welland which operated so satisfactorily that there was no delay to trains of the New York Central Railroad. Gordon countered by saying that he doubted whether that line was ever likely to carry as many trains a day—as the C.N.R. expected to on the Victoria Bridge within a few years. The meeting ended on this inconclusive note. The problem of the Victoria Bridge began to attract the interest of press and public. Just how were we going to reach an amicable and workable agreement? However, Gordon and I did reach agreement. We issued a joint statement to the press at Montreal. Perhaps unfortunately, we did not say *what* agreement we had come to.

Engineers and city officials throughout the city were highly mystified as to what agreement was possible over the bridge. To outside observers, it looked like the classic dilemma of the irresistible force meeting the immovable object. It seemed that either Gordon's trains were delayed or the seaway's ships were queued up for a chance to slip through between trains. Both alternatives were clearly impossible. How did we solve the problem?

The solution was simple, although expensive. Seaway and C.N.R. engineers had puzzled over the Victoria Bridge problem long before I began arguing with Donald Gordon. They realized that raising a long length of the bridge would be far too expensive and that a single vertical lift span would delay trains too much. So they planned a lock under the bridge's approaches. At this

69

point, they designed a vertical lift span. At the other end of the lock, they placed another vertical span, joined to the main bridge by a second bridge which joined the main structure in mid-stream. This meant that when a ship was entering the lock to be hoisted forty feet up to the next level, trains would be routed over the alternative span. When the ship was passing out of the lock, trains would resume their direct line across the bridge. Lawrence Burpee, our assistant chief engineer, played a prominent part in the scheme calculated to avoid highway traffic interruptions.

However, although this was the plan we eventually agreed on, I was still adamant that such expensive additions to the bridge were not all the seaway's responsibility. I argued that Gordon was getting one-third of a new bridge and that we should not be asked to pay for this.

Eventually, it was decided that Cabinet should rule on who should pay. But Cabinet, perhaps out of deference to Gordon's great reputation and record as a public servant, perhaps out of deference to the fact that I was a former cabinet member, delayed ruling on the problem. It was a useful delay and gave tempers a chance to cool.

When we came to deal with the Honoré Mercier Bridge, which joins Ville St. Pierre with the south shore, we were again faced by the traffic interruption problem. Although this bridge does not carry the same amount of traffic as the Jacques Cartier or Victoria, it certainly will do so in the future. Our problem was complicated by the fact that the seaway channel would be cut some distance inland from where the bridge came ashore. The bridge approaches were massive concrete affairs. When the approaches had crossed the seaway, they had to swing in several directions, crossing other roads and the C.P.R. rail line which runs parallel to the Mercier.

The Mercier was one of the few structures along the St. Lawrence River which showed traces of earlier seaway planning. When the bridge was built in the early thirties, it was thought that the seaway—then the subject

70

of many costly engineering surveys—would go along the Montreal shore. The bridge builders, a specially created Quebec commission (La Corporation du Pont du Lac St.-Louis) agreed to install a movable span in the northern section of the bridge when the seaway came through. But the seaway never came. The provisions for the span remain unused to this day. When engineers examined this bridge they found that so tremendous had been the increase in road traffic that a vertical lift span was out of the question anyway.

Again, our responsibility plainly indicated that nothing more than a single lift span was necessary at this point, but this would have created such an uproar in Montreal that we decided to build an entire new section to the bridge, soaring 120 feet above the seaway, then descending to a maze of elevated approaches that branched over the rail lines and other roads. A lift span might have cost us $2 million. The final work cost $12 million.

The other bridges along the seaway—moving upriver —are the C.P.R. bridge at Caughnawaga, about a quarter of a mile west of the Mercier, and the three Beauharnois bridges, all rail structures. Because of the gradient problem and the lighter rail traffic on these bridges, it was possible to plan vertical lift spans knowing they would adequately serve the demands of both rail and ship traffic. The last bridge to affect the seaway is the Cornwall Bridge which crossed the north and south channels of the river and the intervening island at Cornwall.

As Authority officials met hundreds of individuals, committees, and organizations affected by the seaway to discuss mutual problems it rapidly became clear that many people cherished peculiar illusions about us. Many believed the Authority was equipped with an inexhaustible bank account. This money, they thought, could be used to do work which nobody else wanted, or could afford, to do. At one stage, owners of certain expensive houses on Montreal's south shore asked for compensation because we were going to block their view of the river

71

with fill dredged from the channel. We told them that it was not possible to own a view, even though the existence of a view might enhance property values. To cushion their disappointment, we told them we were going to landscape the seaway channel and that the view would be equally attractive afterwards. Property values, we also mentioned, were going up all along the south shore.

The shipping interests feared that the seaway would spoil or outdate their facilities. The Quebec roads department was certain the seaway would cause uncontrollable traffic jams. The press appealed for the Authority to build new wharves and warehouses to complement the channel. To all this, we had to reluctantly reply that our powers were strictly limited. We merely had power to acquire land and build a twenty-seven-foot channel.

During 1955, there was growing pressure in Montreal for the Authority to take some responsibility for the city's traffic problems. The seaway, said the Montrealers, would vastly increase traffic to the city's south shore, and eventually would result in great traffic jams along that shore as trucks and cars struggled to and from the various bridges to the city.

At one stage, representatives of the various interests in Metropolitan Montreal met seaway officials in the Authority's board room to discuss a Montreal plan to defeat these problems. It was proposed that since the seaway would be erecting an enormous sixteen-mile-long causeway along the south shore to protect the seaway channel from the rest of the river, the Authority might just as well pave this and provide the city with a new cheap access highway. This would connect all the south shore from the Mercier Bridge to the Jacques Cartier at downtown Montreal.

It was an ingenious scheme but we had to turn it down. Our engineers reported that serious accidents on the projected highway could result in cars being pitched into thirty feet of water. In winter ice jams would sometimes buckle and fall onto the road.

72

Construction Begins

The Province of Quebec was particularly worried lest the seaway affect its future plans to develop power in Lachine. Would water levels be maintained? Would the flow of water be constant? Would it be possible to develop all potential hydro-electric power in the future? These were a few of the questions asked of Authority officials every day in the early stages of the work. Quebec Hydro was particularly insistent that we do nothing to hurt their existing hydro-generating plant at Beauharnois, or harm their potential power at Lachine. Some of their engineers claimed that seaway construction upriver would hurt existing hydro installations.

At first, there seemed to be no easy answer to these questions. Each question called for complicated engineering calculations to answer them. The answers were sometimes subject to many interpretations. So we decided to make a huge model of the Lachine section of the river. Using this, we would create any situation in miniature and visually answer questions and complaints. Eventually Quebec Hydro became so impressed by the model that they asked whether they might be allowed to use it for their own work. We gladly said yes.

At one stage, at the request of Quebec Hydro, we agreed to divert 40,000 cubic feet per second from the river into our channel during the non-navigation season. This abolished an excess water problem for Montreal largely caused by high spring waters coming down the Ottawa River. We planned to install a small canal, or cut, with an embankment, which would enable us to take exactly the right amount of additional water from the river.

The Province of Quebec was committed, through the determination of Premier Duplessis, to a policy of observation rather than assistance to the St. Lawrence Seaway. However unrealistic we might think this policy was, we had to bear with it and try to understand why it existed. It was, therefore, a pleasant surprise when the observation

73

policy was relaxed a little when we came to the last of the main obstructions at Beauharnois.

Before the seaway was started, Quebec had built a four-lane highway to Beauharnois from the west. It was to continue along the south shore and become a main artery into the city of Montreal. Work on it had stopped when plans for the seaway were finalized. We expected a tussle over which force would have to give way—the highway or the seaway. At one stage during our discussions, Premier Duplessis said, "Your canal, you must understand, is right in the path of my highway. We began the highway first. You cannot expect us to relocate the highway." Then he added, with what must have been Gallic irony, "On the other hand, I appreciate that it would be difficult to relocate your canal. That would cost a lot."

Instead of argument, we got agreement. The Authority was to provide a four-lane tunnel under the seaway lock at Beauharnois just west of the enormous power-house, and Premier Duplessis would give us $300,000 to help with the construction.

The worst problems facing us had been along the densely populated Montreal section of the seaway. After one particularly exhausting day of discussions with a dozen Montrealers, one Authority engineer said, "My next canal will be dug across a desert, a thousand miles from the nearest human habitation." But farther west along the river, there were still severe difficulties awaiting us.

At Cornwall, where the joint power-houses were being built and the huge man-made lake was to back up to Iroquois, the Americans had to do a great deal of dredging south of Cornwall Island. This was to make a channel leading into the first of their locks to lift ships up to the level of the lake.

One of the results of this dredging, together with some dredging we had planned ourselves, was to increase the efficiency of the power-houses. It did this by increasing the "head" of water available. In other words, lowering

74

the river-bed below the power-houses had the effect of raising the height of water above them. The result was more power.

So when the dredging arrangements were being jointly discussed, we suggested that the two Power Authorities pay for some of this dredging. At first, they refused, even though they admitted they would benefit from the dredging. Eventually, Ontario Hydro agreed to pay $12 million and they split the bill with the N.Y. Power Authority.

While we were discussing the problems of dredging at Cornwall with the Americans, we received an invitation from the Secretary of the Army, Wilbur Brucker, to visit the Panama Canal to examine how the canal handled dredging and lockage problems. The Panama Canal is administered by the U.S. Corps of Engineers. These engineers were to be in charge of all seaway construction on the American side.

Gavsie, West, Murphy and I flew down to Washington and took the Secretary of the Army's airplane to Panama. On the flight down, we got into an argument over the Cornwall dredging. In the extensive dredging the U.S. had to do south of Cornwall Island, so much material would be removed that the flow of the river would be unbalanced. The existing flow was 33⅓ per cent north of Cornwall Island, the rest south of Cornwall Island. The dredging would change this rate to 20 per cent north of the island and 80 per cent south of it. One of the top U.S. engineers had a plan whereby we could equalize the flow by digging a big hole in the bed of the river just north of the island.

"Actually," I said, "we've more or less decided to dredge a full twenty-seven-foot channel along there."

"What!" he said. "That's a hell of a way to do things. What do you need with such a big channel? It's just a waste of money."

"Sure," I said, "We have the right to do as we please in our own territory."

"But you don't need it," he said.

75

"We will need it when we build duplicate facilities on our side of the river," I said.

With that, he stated we were not playing fair with the U.S. and that it was against all agreements between the two countries. At all costs, he wanted to discourage us from digging a duplicate channel. But we remained adamant. We ignored his plan for "a big hole" on our side. It was patently a device to prevent the digging of the deep channel. Later, we went a step further. When the 100-foot-high dyke was being built to dam up the water for the power development, we installed two concrete abutments in the dyke. They were large enough to accept the full seaway-size channel at a later date. They were to be blocked up temporarily with stop logs. They served to protect Canada's right to build duplicate facilities on our side as and when the Canadian Government so decided.

One of the American seaway officials later saw this construction for the first time and he was horrified. "What have you done?" he said to an Authority official. "If the word gets around Washington at this stage that you're planning a Canadian seaway, it could be embarrassing for all of us." Later he approached Dr. Otto Holden, then chief of Ontario Hydro, and asked whether there was any possibility of covering up the abutments. But the abutments remained. When the all-Canadian seaway is eventually built, this forethought will save many millions of dollars.

When we reached Panama, the engineers guiding us over the canal spent some time showing how efficient the mechanical "mules" were in pulling ships through the canal. These mules run along the side of the locks and pull ships from lock to lock. They are an expensive but effective method of keeping traffic on the move. Later, the engineers suggested that we incorporate this mule system into the seaway, but both the U.S. and Canada turned down the idea. We arranged a reciprocal visit for the American seaway officials to our Welland Canal—the

76

Construction Begins

locks of which are nearly as big as Panama—and showed them that traffic can move just as quickly without the mules.

During the Cornwall Island dredging discussions, we had to decide what to do with the New York Central Railroad line which crossed the river south of Cornwall, ran across Cornwall Island, then crossed the south channel over a low-level bridge into the U.S. The Americans were going to dredge the river-bed at the bridge-site. The first plans suggested that the railway should be diverted west on Cornwall Island, cross a channel (Polly's Gut) to the U.S., run some distance west, turn south, cross the American seaway at the Eisenhower Lock, cross the Grass River, then turn east to rejoin its old road-bed.

I was surprised during one of my field trips to discover that a new highway had been built from Massena to Polly's Gut and ended at the water's edge in apparent anticipation of a bridge that, so far, I knew nothing about. Some inquiries established what had happened. The ebullient and energetic chairman of the Power Authority of the State of New York, Robert Moses—well known for his park-building schemes—had suggested to Lewis Castle that the railroad should be diverted over Polly's Gut. The object of the diversion was to make it easier for people to visit the great parkland scheme which Moses was even then building round the U.S. canal system. Moses calculated that he could use the projected rail bridge across Polly's Gut to bring road traffic as well to his parklands from the Canadian side. Castle had agreed to this plan because it would not only take rail passengers to the parklands, but it would also give them an excellent view of the American section of the seaway.

Unfortunately, there was another side of the question. Five miles to the east of the N.Y.C. rail line lived several hundred Indians at St. Regis, Quebec. These people used Cornwall as their shopping and education centre. The new rail diversion would mean their travelling an additional five miles. When we came to calculate the comparative costs, it turned out that the diversion was going to cost nearly two million dollars more than by installing a suspension bridge over the south channel on the existing route. After some discussions with the Americans they agreed that the straight-line route was more practical, and the diversion scheme was cancelled. Moses was most chagrined. He made some pungent and public comments about Castle which I thought were unfair. But Castle stood his ground and fought back. Moses' road still ends at the edge of Polly's Gut and I imagine it will be some years before the traffic there warrants a bridge.

These were the sort of difficulties that the two parties encountered before building the seaway. They were severe tests of the patience and tolerance of both parties. Many times we had occasion to be grateful that the Americans—despite their occasional impetuosity—were capable of extraordinary compromise and reasonableness.

Construction Begins

CHAPTER SIX

THE WORK GOES FORWARD

Excavation

Lachine Construction

Drying Up the Rapids

Construction of the Power Project

Thousand Islands and the Welland

EXCAVATION

Construction of the St. Lawrence Seaway has been compared with the building of the Panama Canal. Both were enormous enterprises. But their size is their only real similarity. Panama took more than twenty years of wrangling, bitterness, bankruptcy, corruption and bribery to complete. The seaway was built in four years and was never off schedule. Panama is uneconomic, may never pay for itself. The seaway is a coldly realistic proposition which will pay for itself in less than fifty years.

There is, perhaps, another point of similarity between the two enterprises. The Panama Canal builders were nearly defeated by yellow fever. The Panama only became a possibility when the mosquitoes which carried the fever were exterminated. The builders of the seaway struck a much more prosaic problem which at times seemed nearly as bad as the Panamanian mosquitoes of half a century ago. They encountered rock, clay and other types of geological formation which were much

80

The Work Goes Forward

more difficult to remove than they had estimated. Their difficulties with this material provided the seaway administration with some of its biggest headaches.

I should explain that our method of choosing construction firms to build the seaway was the same as that used throughout industry. The Seaway Authority would publish a list of specifications of the work we wanted done and the date we wanted it done by. These jobs were then competed for by any construction companies in Canada which felt fitted to tackle them.

This usually meant that dozens of firms were bidding against one another, each one seeking to bid as low as possible. But at the same time, in making such bids, the construction firms were gambling against the risks that lay ahead. Presumably, they were including in their bids some insurance against such risks.

Soon after work began, it became apparent that something had gone wrong. Our engineers on site were told

81

that the material being uncovered in excavation work at some points was unbelievably tough and difficult to dig out. Shovel teeth and bulldozer blades, which can last for a year or more in easy conditions, were wearing out in days, or even hours. Drills for boring through rock were worn out in four or five feet of drilling, instead of fifty or sixty feet. One company imported a jet-impelled boring machine which blasted a 4,000-degree flame into the rock till it was white-hot, then douched it with cold water. The rock, suddenly cooled, would shatter and literally explode out of the hole in a cloud of steam.

But who can instantly judge, at that early stage, whether a contractor is exaggerating the bad conditions he is striking? Certainly I could not. Years later, in September, 1958, the *Engineering Journal*, published by the Engineering Institute of Canada, reported on this phase of our work, "Bidders on early contracts on both sides of the river, particularly in excavation, bid on the work at prices generally far too low to show them a profit. This was due in part to their desire to become associated with a project destined to get much publicity, and in part to lack of judgment with respect to cost of handling the heavy marine clay and dense till in the foundations."

When the first complaints about bad excavating conditions began reaching me, I said that these conditions were the responsibility of the contractors. Before they made their bids, they had had plenty of opportunity to test the ground to be excavated. It was their risk. They retorted that it was impossible to foresee every eventuality. But I felt strongly that they should only be permitted to adjust their positions through the courts—not by private agreement.

Whatever the real facts behind the problems of this period—too low bidding, unpredictably tough rock, poor preparation for the work—the excavating contractors said flatly that they were not being justly and equably treated. Three American contractors went bankrupt and their work was let out again at much higher prices. The

The Work Goes Forward

Americans had a lot of trouble with glacial till, a compacted type of earth that resembles rock. This was overlaid by a thick layer of gumbo clay which bogged down all heavy machines. Before the contractors could even get to the work-sites, they had to build expensive roads. These conditions forced one big American construction firm, which had contracted to excavate a large section of the Long Sault canal, to seek nearly double its original estimate to complete the job. On the Canadian side, contractors also had trouble with glacial till and many difficulties arose between them and the Authority over it.

The urgency of the job, which was most apparent at the construction site of the giant U.S.-Canadian power-houses just up the river from Cornwall, was shown in some of the construction methods used. The Canadians, lacking the sheer number of men and machines that the giant American construction companies could muster, were forced to use emergency methods to get their contracts completed in time.

During one winter, when construction on the American side had slowed to a standstill in sub-zero temperatures, the Canadian builders kept hard at work. One of the American engineers, watching heated concrete being poured into the power-house foundations, said, "I hope those fellows know what they're doing. Our men won't pour if the temperature goes below zero."

The Canadians knew what they were doing. Their winter experience kept them at work. They even poured concrete in thirty- and forty-feet lots—as opposed to the American additions of about six feet at a time.

One of the features of the seaway construction was that most of the big jobs were taken by groups of big contractors banded together into composite companies, specially formed for doing seaway contracts. This was done for two reasons. It was known, for a start, that bidding on the seaway would be intensely competitive. Dozens, perhaps hundreds of firms, would be seeking sea-

83

Excavation

way jobs—not for the profit, but for the prestige of being able to say that they participated in the biggest construction job in Canada. When this sort of situation occurs in construction, it is difficult for contractors to make a profit. Some even go bankrupt trying to do large jobs too cheaply.

The companies decided in advance that since low bidding prices would be common they might as well spread the work as widely as possible, and bid as low as was economically feasible. The result: extremely low prices and extremely high quality of workmanship. To my knowledge, there were no examples of shoddy work on the entire seaway job, which is unusual for a project of such magnitude.

There were humorous moments in construction. When work was being done near Laprairie, one contractor was astounded to dredge up a long stretch of railway track running across the river—underwater. The track broke before it had all been hauled to the surface, but for some hours there was much head-scratching while the men tried to figure out what the underwater rail line meant. The explanation was simple. Laprairie used to be the terminus of the St. Johns Railway and during the winter the railway frequently used to run a spur line across the ice to Montreal. Apparently one year the rail company had delayed taking up the tracks a little too long.

The safety record of the job was surprisingly good but there were unavoidable accidents. As we began digging the channel at Montreal, an embankment, or dyke, was thrown up on the river side. This had to withstand great pressures of water and ice while the machines behind it were scouring out the channel to its full depth of twenty-seven feet. One of the Authority engineers, after examining a huge banked-up mass of ice near a section of this dyke one winter, went down into the excavated channel to see whether the weight of material pushing against the dyke had weakened it at all. As he reached the bottom of the channel, the dyke burst and hundreds of tons of

84

The Work Goes Forward

water and ice poured into the channel. So great was the rush of water that the unfortunate engineer's body was found one mile upstream.

To many engineers who visited seaway construction, it was a surprise that we planned to do so much work in only four years. Even allowing for modern methods and equipment, this would, they said, be a remarkable feat. The Welland Ship Canal, by no means as big, took twelve years. But most of them did not realize that we were forced to work quickly. The Ontario and New York demand for power, which set the tempo, was extremely useful to us. I am sure it pleased chief engineer Murphy, who liked to see work going as rapidly as possible. It was a constant incentive to keep construction on schedule, regardless of the difficulties.

LACHINE CONSTRUCTION

About half of all the money we spent on the seaway in Canada went into the Lachine section, south and south-west of the city of Montreal. It was by far the most complicated part of the job because of the length of the rapids that we had to by-pass and the fact that we were trying to dig a channel through a heavily populated area.

The seaway passes Montreal on the south side of the river. But the first attempt to by-pass the Lachine Rapids —made by Dollier de Casson towards the end of the seventeenth century—was on the north side. When the Lachine Canal was finally completed, it cut across what is now Verdun and Lachine, thickly populated Montreal suburbs.

Why did we not build on the north side, too? Seaway plans of only seven years before envisaged a seaway on the Montreal side. The main reason was the enormous and rapid growth of that side. We wanted to get away from this congestion, and allow the port of Montreal to develop on both shores. Then we knew that the St.

85

Mary's current made navigation and construction work difficult in the crowded harbour area just above the Jacques Cartier Bridge. Lastly, it was known that drastic changes would have to be made to four Montreal bridges. It was far better to be forced to make these adjustments on the less crowded south shore than try to do it on the north where the bridges came ashore into a congested mass of buildings, houses, warehouses, factories and power lines.

The only clear way to give an impression of the work that had to be done here is to begin at the Jacques Cartier Bridge and survey the construction step by step till the top of the Lachine Rapids is reached.

The huge seaway channel is cut into the river 1,000 feet from the south shore opposite Montreal Harbour and it winds past St. Lambert, Laprairie, Côte Ste. Catherine and on up to the Indian village of Caughnawaga by the Lachine Rapids. The seaway winds partly round Montreal and isolates, figuratively speaking, the south shore behind an enormous trench 50 or 60 feet deep and over 200 feet wide. The trench effectively cut off all water intakes and sewage outlets for the south shore.

Before we began digging, we met members of all the municipalities on the south shore and discussed the effects of the channel. Some were disturbed at the possible danger to health. We explained our responsibilities both as to water supplies and sewage disposal during construction. When they learned we intended building a main collector sewer running along seaway territory to hook up to all municipal outflows, there was instant demand from municipalities some distance inland for connection to this sewer. Some even wanted us to install new sewer systems for them. As politely as possible, we refused. But we did tell the municipalities adjacent to the seaway that though we were building them a new sewer, we did not intend to maintain it for them. Only one municipality seemed disposed to accept responsibility to maintain its section of the sewer. For a time,

86

The Work Goes Forward

it looked as though the Seaway Authority was going to be forced into the real estate and sewage business.

One of the unexpected results of digging the channel was that it lowered the water-table for the entire south shore. For most people this did not matter. But hundreds of families had wells. When the water-table dropped to the level of the channel bottom, their water disappeared automatically. We had to keep these people supplied with water from tank wagons until we could connect them to main water supplies. At one stage during construction, we had to set up special pumping plants and temporary water supply lines to keep the citizens of many south shore municipalities supplied with water.

The planning necessary to keep everybody in water was considerable. I do not think anybody went short of water and by the time construction was finished, all the south shore had new water intakes and outlets, along with some handsome new pumping stations big enough to handle expansion many years into the future.

All this work helped St. Lambert, Preville and La-prairie. Previously, these areas suffered from flooding when the river backed up because of ice jams. This is no longer possible. The works along the south shore, although a headache, eventually proved to be of benefit to everybody.

The seaway channel begins at the Jacques Cartier Bridge. Looking up the river, down-town Montreal is on the right, St. Lambert on the left. The bridge, which comes across the river at a height of about 60 feet from the water, unexpectedly starts to climb about four spans from the canal until by the time it crosses the canal it is a clear 120 feet from the water.

Behind that graceful rise of the bridge, lies a fascinating story of human ingenuity. In our preliminary discussions over the bridge, we had learned how it was impossible to think of installing a vertical lift span or to interrupt traffic for more than a few hours. The problem was solved jointly by the Authority and the Dominion Bridge

87

Company which had built the bridge in 1929. By a curious chance, the designer of the bridge, Dr. P. L. Pratley, of Montreal, was working in a consulting capacity for the St. Lawrence Seaway Authority during the construction of the seaway.

He calculated that the only way to dispose of the problem was to jack up the bridge till enough height was achieved to let ships underneath. This meant a direct lift of around fifty feet. But although jacking up several thousand tons of bridge is feasible, eventually jacking becomes impossible because the bridge is "stretched" to its limit. Dr. Pratley got round this difficulty by designing one new span in the multi-span bridge. This span, longer and stronger, had its arched span above the roadway level instead of beneath it. The new span was erected alongside the span it was to replace in readiness for a quick changeover.

But to jack up the bridge, thronged with hundreds of cars, trucks and buses, was not easy. Dominion Bridge used specially designed climbing jacks, each with a lifting capacity of 500 tons. Four of these jacks were set up on each massive concrete pier supporting the bridge. In a synchronized operation, the four jacks pushed the span up six inches at a time. Precast concrete blocks were then manoeuvred into position under the jacks so that when the jacks were lowered the bridge rested on the blocks. This operation was repeated hundreds of times along the fourteen spans that had to be lifted.

The jacking had to be precise. In fifty feet of lifting a small error would be magnified to serious proportions. The precast concrete blocks were actually finished to a tolerance of $\frac{1}{64}$ of an inch. Some of the jacking had to be done at night, when traffic was light. Heavy traffic creates what the engineers called "a live load" which makes the bridge tremble and which might have been dangerous.

As the jacking reached its peak of fifty feet, a falsework was constructed alongside the span to be replaced

88

The Work Goes Forward

and the new span was built on top of the falsework. This had to be designed in such a way that the existing span could be replaced by the new one with great speed. Even a day's delay to traffic would cause chaos in Montreal.

When the new span was slipped into place, amid great public fanfare, it was of course overlong for that section, but several weeks of steady jacking remained and by the time it was completed, the bridge had "shrunk" because of its greater height, and the span fitted easily into the places provided for it. This project was, as I announced to the press, undoubtedly "one of the most spectacular and complicated works required for the St. Lawrence Seaway". It attracted the attention of engineers all over the world. It cost nearly $7 million.

Some engineers have commented that the alteration has vastly improved the appearance of the bridge, and hence the appearance of the harbour. Previously, the bridge was a somewhat undistinguished structure, hugging the river closely. But now, it rises to a graceful peak over the canal before sweeping down again to St. Lambert and the shore.

Underneath the raised bridge go the beginnings of the deep channel that, in one form or another, does not end till Lake Erie more than 300 miles away. The channel itself, entirely man-made, snakes along the south shore for about ten miles till it reaches Côte Ste. Catherine at the foot of the Lachine Rapids. The channel then goes overland past the rapids and opens into Lake St. Louis.

The embankment which separates the canal from the river carries a hard-surfaced road. From the Jacques Cartier Bridge to the Victoria Bridge, Montreal's other down-town bridge, is a distance of about 10,000 feet. At this bridge, almost directly beneath one of its shore spans, is the first lock in the seaway. It was built there to overcome yet another bridge problem. It was a problem that plagued us all up the river.

The Victoria Bridge carries both road and rail traffic. This means that it cannot be jacked up like the Jacques

89

Cartier. The gradient would be too steep for the 120-odd trains that pass over it every day. And yet, like the Jacques Cartier, it was impossible to stop traffic for more than a few hours. Lawrence Burpee's solution to the problem was, in my opinion, as ingenious as the alteration to the Jacques Cartier.

The fact that an embankment was being built the full length of this Lachine section of the river meant that the canal behind it was quite independent of the rise and fall of river water on the other side. This meant that we could locate our two locks on this section—necessary to raise ships about 60 feet above the rapids—at almost any place along the channel. The residents of Montreal must have wondered what was going on at the Victoria Bridge during the reconstruction there. A maze of roads twisted in and out of deep cuts, enormous concrete structures, temporary bridges and looming cranes.

I reflected one day when I drove across the bridge that the reconstruction project was fully as complicated and confusing as the negotiations with C.N.R. president Donald Gordon had been. To confuse the mind even further, during construction, it seemed that the men were actually building another bridge across the river. But it was pointed the wrong way. It was obviously going to run diagonally into the existing bridge several hundred yards from the shore. This was part of the plan devised to permit unrestricted entry and exit of Montreal rail and road traffic via the vertical lift spans at each end of the lock.

It is interesting to imagine a ship going through this lock. As the ship approaches the lock from downstream, the first vertical lift is raised and the lock gates are opened. At this lock the ship is raised approximately 21½ feet. Meanwhile, all road and rail traffic has been diverted to the other bridge approach which contains the second lift at the other end of the lock. It is this approach to the bridge that moves out across the water

90

The Work Goes Forward

diagonally to join up with the original bridge several hundreds yards off shore.

Then with the ship safely inside the lock, the lock gates are shut, the vertical lift is lowered, and traffic resumes its original route across the bridge *behind* the ship. The ship is free to be raised to the next level, the upper gates opened, the second vertical lift raised, and so on up the river.

Ahead, the channel takes a wide sweeping curve round the southern limits of the Laprairie Basin and heads towards the foot of the Lachine Rapids and the next lock— the Côte Ste. Catherine. This lock was specially designed to handle the varying water-levels which occur in Lake St. Louis as well as to hoist ships a further 36½ feet up the river. About six miles in the distance two bridges can be seen, the Honoré Mercier and a C.P.R. bridge. Construction problems here were not so acute as lower down the river. It was relatively easy for the approaches of the Mercier to be raised and a 120-foot span installed while the C.P.R. rail bridge was fitted with two vertical lift spans.

Again it was essential that traffic be uninterrupted on the Mercier Bridge. This posed a problem because the bridge came ashore and began sloping gently to ground level long before it reached the site of the proposed seaway channel. Its substantial concrete approaches actually crossed the channel site. These approaches had to be demolished and a 120-foot-high bridge installed instead. The contractor blew up the approaches in one great blast. This, of course, meant interruption of traffic. The contractor got around the problem by building a huge earthen ramp running alongside the new construction and cutting onto the bridge at the riverside.

On the right of the seaway channel, going upriver, the foaming white-caps of the Lachine Rapids can be seen and the canal is nearly ready to let the ship onto Lake St. Louis. As the open water is about to begin, the channel goes carefully round the Indian village of Caugh-

Lachine Construction

nawaga. Visitors to the Jesuit mission there can look over the earth ramparts built in 1760 down onto the decks of a passing freighter.

St. Louis is a pleasant lake, but despite its size—about fifteen miles long by seven wide—it needed extensive dredging to take the channel to the next section of the construction work—the Soulanges section. Perhaps some of this shallowness is due to the Ottawa River draining into the north-western corner of the lake.

At the beginning of this Soulanges section, the river splits. On the far right, on an isthmus of land, the Federally-built Soulanges Canal—fourteen feet deep and a masterpiece in its day—used to take canallers overland past the Soulanges Rapids into Lake St. Francis. Dead ahead is the main channel of the river and the rapids. On the left is a gigantic power-house. Behind it is one of the wonders of the seaway valley, a man-made channel 3,300 feet wide and sixteen miles long.

The Beauharnois Light, Heat & Power Company actually began this section of the seaway in 1929 by building this huge overland canal to get enough pressure of water to provide power for Montreal Light, Heat & Power Company. This power was first delivered on October 1, 1932.

During the construction of the power canal, the work was declared to be for the general advantage of Canada by Federal legislation. In other words, the government realized that while so much constructional work was being done in the area, it would be a good time to extend the works and prepare for the seaway.

The legislation obligated the power company to transfer to Canada the title to the bed of the power canal which was to be dredged across farmland. In the bed of the canal, the power company had to construct a navigation channel 600 feet wide, 27 feet deep with a very slow rate of water flow—about 240,000 cubic feet a second. It also had to build the substructures of two combined railway and highway crossings which would allow lift

92

The Work Goes Forward

bridges to be installed by Canada when the canal was finally opened to ocean-going ships. By the time the excavation work was finished and a gigantic power-house had been erected, the Beauharnois company had dug more ground than the builders of the Panama Canal.

The height of the water in this dammed-up section of the river was eighty feet and we had to build two locks alongside the Beauharnois power-house to get the ships to the next stage of the river. It was here that contractors struck the fault of sandstone and wore out so much of their equipment. They also showed considerable ingenuity. At the lower end of the canal passing the power-house, two substantial approach walls were necessary. Visitors to one of the locks during construction were surprised to see huge concrete "tanks" crowding the channel below the lock. These were constructed on site and left there in readiness for the release of water into the lock from the river. The "tanks" would then float, be manoeuvred into position in the place of the wall and sunk in position. It was a simple solution to a time-consuming job of constructing an embankment.

Apart from the problems of the rock in this area, the other difficulties were routine. The contractors had to move about 750,000 cubic yards of concrete, build a four-lane highway tunnel under the lower lock (helped by Mr. Duplessis' $300,000) to maintain uninterrupted car and truck travel, divert the New York Central Railroad while concrete was poured at the upper end of the lock, and install two vertical lift bridges.

At the western end of the Beauharnois Power Canal is Lake St. Francis, a larger version of Lake St. Louis. From this lake, we removed about four and a half million cubic yards of earth by dredging to give a twenty-seven-foot channel about 450 feet wide. At the end of this lake are the longest rapids on the St. Lawrence—the International Rapids section of the river.

One day in 1957, the last section of a coffer dam—a series of earth-filled steel tanks—was completed at the head of the Long Sault Rapids. The dam stretched from Canadian soil to Long Sault Island on U.S. territory. It began diverting water across a giant man-made cut in the island. Gradually, the water flow down the famous Long Sault Rapids decreased and rocks began humping out of the water where before there had been white-caps and fierce turbulence. In a few hours, the water had gone and inquisitive people began picking their way among the rocks, attracted by the possibility of some valuable find. Most of them thought the rapids might have caught and held cargo of wrecked ships. But they were disappointed. There was nothing of value left in the empty river-bed.

This was the beginning of a series of man-made alterations to nature in this area which were to become famous throughout the world. It is difficult to give a visual picture of this area in words because the work covered such a vast area and consisted of so many separate enterprises. But broadly, the area in which the work was done extended from Cornwall up the river for fifty miles. This is one of the most beautiful sections of the St. Lawrence. It is what you might call the tail end of the Thousand Island section of the river. Before work was begun it consisted of many large and small islands and a series of rapids, the largest being the Long Sault. In this fifty miles the river fell ninety feet, which permitted the development of over two million horsepower of electricity, while navigation was not impeded.

It was planned that the navigation channel would be dug along the south bank by the Americans. The power would be developed by creating a 100-square-mile lake along the north bank. This lake would submerge the Long Sault Rapids and about 28,000 acres of farmland. The navigation channel would by-pass this lake and ships

94

The Work Goes Forward

would steam into the lake after being hoisted up eighty feet by two American locks. Meanwhile, the flooding of the lake would stretch back nearly thirty miles, allowing ships to reach Iroquois before another lock was necessary. Here it was necessary to build another dam, at Iroquois, to control the level of Lake Ontario.

The technique of construction in the International Section was ingenious. It consisted simply of thrusting the river's flow from the main north channel into the smaller southern channel via the coffer dam. This dried up the Long Sault Rapids and left the river-bed clear to build the power-houses near Cornwall and a control dam joining Barnhart Island and the American mainland. While this was being done, the Americans began building their great overland channel with its two locks immediately south of Barnhart and Long Sault Islands. They took about 36 million cubic yards of material out of the trench, then poured more than a million cubic yards of concrete into the locks. Further upriver, they dredged millions of cubic yards from the bed of the river. Theirs was perhaps the most concentrated piece of construction along the entire route. When they had finished the Long Sault dam, and the power-houses were finished, the river valley was ready for flooding.

CONSTRUCTION OF THE POWER PROJECT

During the construction of the seaway, it was frequently necessary for its builders to remind themselves that there were two major projects under way. Possibly the more glamorous, the more headline-catching, part of the work was the navigation channel. This interested the trading and manufacturing world as well as the consumer because a deep channel would likely make many products easier to obtain, cheaper to buy. The industrial world, on the other hand, eagerly watched the electrical side of the seaway. A small rise in the cost of electricity could

95

involve large industrial enterprises in increased costs of millions of dollars a year. The seaway promised to delay this by providing a vast quantity of cheap power.

The Power Authority of the State of New York, which shared the work with the Hydro Electric Power Commission of Ontario, made a report on August 10, 1954, which summed up the work that had to be done at that time. The report said, in part:

". . . The project will consist of two major dams, the powerhouse structure (which is also a dam), power generating and transforming facilities, extensive channel works, and dikes and wing dams as required. It will be necessary to relocate main highways, railroads and navigation facilities, as well as homes and businesses within the forebay pool area. Access by railroad and highway, and construction camps will require extensive works of a temporary nature. An existing low-head plant at Massena, New York, will be abandoned to permit use of that water in the more efficient, higher-head project plant. Certain plants on the Canadian side will be similarly affected.

"Overall, some 86 million cubic yards of excavation will be required in the construction of the various features, including five million cubic yards of dry rock and 31 million cubic yards of earth and rock to be removed underwater. The embankments and cofferdams will contain 19 million cubic yards of earth and rock, and the dams and power-house will contain some three million cubic yards of concrete and 190 million pounds of reinforcing steel and structural shapes."

The two builders agreed to share the power available equally, to share the amount of construction works equally, and, excepting the cost of the power-house equipment and machinery, do exactly half of all the work within the territory of each country. This was calculated to eliminate arguments or misunderstandings. This turned out to be impractical, the result being that the Power Authority of the State of New York actually undertook

96

The Work Goes Forward

considerably more of the physical work than did Ontario Hydro. However, when it came to dredging the channel, of which the Power Authority had to do 32 million cubic yards and Ontario Hydro 23 million cubic yards, nobody became too worried when U.S. dredges had to dredge Canadian soil and Canadian dredges work on U.S. soil.

The crux of the power development along the International Rapids section is Barnhart Island which used to stand firmly astride the river allowing the water to flow on either side of it. Its north channel was bounded by Sheek Island where I swam as a youngster and the Long Sault Rapids were just a little farther up the river from the two islands. Barnhart was the key because at that point the main flow of the river was narrow, while the ground on either side was relatively high. It would be a simple matter, the engineers calculated, to build a power-house across the river and extend an embankment for several miles on either side of it. This would result in a really impressive back-up of water.

The only additional construction needed to make this possible was to dam up the other channel which formerly ran south of Barnhart Island. But before this could be done, the south channel somehow had to be emptied to permit the construction of the diversionary dam. So the coffer dam was built at the head of the rapids, diverting the water round Long Sault Island. This enabled the builders to construct half the Long Sault Dam. Then the water was released through the dam while the other half of it was built. When finished, the Long Sault Dam consisted of more than 7 million yards of excavation, 657,000 cubic yards of concrete, 10,000,000 pounds of steel for gantries and gates.

In the meantime, Ontario Hydro was grappling with a valley-sized public relations problem. The commission is jealous of its public service role in the community. It was, therefore, with considerable distaste that Hydro officials had to go up and down the valley and tell 6,500 people that they had lost their farms, homes and busi-

97

nesses. Their land, the Hydro men said, would be buried under deep water forever. Some families had lived on the land for 175 years or more and Ontario Hydro's task of persuasion was sometimes difficult.

I was invited to the opening ceremonies of the power project which took place on July 1, 1958. Dr. Otto Holden, Ontario Hydro's chief engineer, pressed a button which ignited thirty tons of dynamite and blew up the coffer dam. The explosion and the flooding were perhaps an anticlimax to the 20,000 people who lined the embankments nearby, but for the Hydro men it was the biggest moment in the commission's history. The power-house, a push-button marvel that is connected to many points upriver by telephone, radio-telephone and by various automatic telemetering devices, is even equipped with a picture theatre (for showing educational films), and observation lounges. I was chatting with Dr. Holden after the opening and he said he had never seen a power-house like it anywhere else in the world.

THOUSAND ISLANDS AND THE WELLAND

Upstream past the International Rapids, the bulk of the work is now left behind once Iroquois and its dam and the Canadian lock are passed. Ahead lies the Thousand Islands section. For 65 miles through this beautiful area, dredges worked from 1954 to 1959 deepening the channels to the full regulation 27-foot seaway depth and 450-foot width. The Authority and the U.S. Development Corporation co-operated on this work. From Brockville to Lake Ontario, the channel is almost entirely in U.S. territory and needed extensive deepening. It is perhaps ironic that the wealthy U.S. should be deprived of much of the glamour of constructing the seaway. Millions of dollars of the U.S. contribution went into dredging.

The remaining share of Canada's work was not much

98

The Work Goes Forward

more glamorous, but it involved a historic canal—the Welland. When the Welland Ship Canal was completed in 1932 at a cost of $132 million, the depth was 25 feet. Now we had to establish a controlling depth of 27 feet throughout without interrupting shipping movements. This was a complex, heart-breaking job at times, even though much of the excavation work was done in winter when the canal was drained. Altogether 2,300,000 cubic yards of shallow rock dredging was done along the Welland and ship traffic was not held up for a moment.

Contractors working on the Welland faced peculiar problems. How could they, for instance, excavate close to the retaining walls of the canal? When using explosives, essential along much of the rock bottom, it was impossible to loosen material closer than fourteen feet from retaining walls. Although this is fairly satisfactory, it leaves a piece of ground jutting under water from the wall. This is enough to prevent ships from mooring against the wall.

The contractors used an ingenious new system of blasting developed by Canadian Industries Ltd. The company had found that air-filled spaces cushioned explosive blasts. Acting on this simple fact, the contractors were able to drill holes almost right alongside concrete walls, fit hermetically sealed cans into the holes, and blast fifty to sixty tons of rock loose at one time, the rock breaking up to within a couple of feet from the wall. The cans absorbed the blast and the rock broke cleanly along the line of holes. The system was also used, in slightly different form, for blasting rock in midstream. Normally, during blasting, the barge from which the blast holes are being drilled and the explosives set, has to move away from the firing site or be damaged by the underwater explosion.

The "air cushion" principle was found to be just as effective when air bubbles were used in place of tin cans. A compressor was fitted to the barges doing the blasting and provided a curtain of bubbles rising up the side of

99

the ship. The contractors were then able to blast 100 tons of rock loose at one explosion only 30 feet from the barge. The millions of tiny bubbles totally absorbed the explosion.

The construction of the St. Lawrence Seaway was an historic project. It was an unforgettable experience for the thousands who helped build it and saw the St. Lawrence Valley changed to suit the purposes of the people of Canada and the United States.

The Work Goes Forward

CHAPTER SEVEN

MOVING THE PEOPLE

One Hundred Square Miles Expropriated

Persuading the Iroquois

Moving Old Settlements

The Models

ONE HUNDRED SQUARE MILES EXPROPRIATED

During the building of the seaway, an old Indian stolidly waited inside his house near Montreal while construction men pleaded with him to move. Outside, bulldozers waited to begin work. On another part of the seaway's course, an angry farmer, on learning he was to lose his farm, took a shotgun from the wall and threatened to blast a Seaway Authority employee to pieces. In another instance, valuers had to tabulate a history of each tree in an orchard in an effort to settle a dispute over the orchard's value.

For several thousand people, the coming of the seaway was a difficult and challenging period. About 100 square miles of land, much of it agriculturally rich, had to be expropriated before we could begin work. Some people simply did not want to be expropriated.

When a Crown company equipped with expropriative powers declares a piece of land is needed for its purposes, and registers a notice of expropriation, the land auto-

102

Moving the People

matically ceases to be the property of the existing land-owner. But he does retain the right to compensation and to dispute the amount offered.

The task of assessors is frequently difficult because of the peculiar factors that may affect the price of land. A man may have saved money carefully all his life for his old age. At his retirement, he may have had the good luck to find a piece of property that will allow him to earn just enough to live for the rest of his life without too much work. Then the seaway, or some other govern-ment project, takes the land from him. He argues that he cannot replace it at the same price. He will also say that he will never be able to recreate the conditions he had.

The assessors carefully consider all possible factors to make their valuation. People expropriated must be able to re-establish themselves. One man who had bought a small store and farmlet on the south shore of Montreal refused to accept offers for his land or even talk about

103

One Hundred Square Miles Expropriated

moving. He said he could not buy another farm so close to Montreal so exactly fitted to his needs. However, a routine offer was made for the property. Almost immediately, the man found an almost identical property nearby, accepted the expropriation offer, and ended up with almost $5,000 more in the bank than when he started. Property owners facing expropriation tended to see it as the end of the world. In the International Rapids section, Ontario Hydro, in expropriating 6,500 people, took the most elaborate care to make sure that everybody was treated fairly and humanely. Hydro is skilled at this work, but the Seaway Authority was not. In the relatively small amount of expropriation work we had to do, we used the lands division of the Department of Transport. The method of operation was for the division to write the landowners and tell them that the land was needed and that somebody would call on them. Then a man from the division would call on a preliminary visit to make the acquaintance of the landowner. Subsequently, he would call again and make an offer for the property.

At the western end of the construction at Montreal, just before the seaway opens into Lake St. Louis, there is the Indian village of Caughnawaga. It is situated on a piece of land that juts on to the river almost due south of the entrance to the old Lachine Canal. It is an historic place, the site of an early Jesuit mission in North America. Old fortifications are still preserved there. The village is not large but its people are noted for their contributions to the construction business. Indian high-scaffold men are much in demand in New York where they work fearlessly and well at great heights.

When we first began our surveying and expropriation proceedings at Caughnawaga, the great majority of the people were satisfied with what we were doing. But it was not going to be that simple. The Indians, perhaps with some prompting, took the position that here was a chance to make some money out of the seaway. Their rights were being violated and they did not lack an ap-

104

Moving the People

preciation of public relations. They staged war-dances against the seaway and captured big headlines in the Montreal newspapers which gave the impression that the problems at Caughnawaga were much bigger than they really were.

All kinds of rumours circulated around the village. It was said, for instance, that the seaway channel would be built straight along the main street of the village. The entire community would be wiped out. Another story said that the Indians would get paid less than white landowners farther down the river. The Indians were certainly led to believe that the more fuss and trouble they made the more money they would get. I do not think we ever managed to convince them that this was not true. The Indian who stayed in his house till the construction crews were ready to begin work was a good example of this misguided attitude. Land values are decided impartially, and if there is a dispute, it goes to court. But sometimes I felt that the Indians were just having a lot of fun at the expense of the seaway.

PERSUADING THE IROQUOIS

On one occasion I was invited by the Indians to attend a friendly and informal meeting in the village and to meet most of the leading citizens there. I decided this was an excellent opportunity to tell them just what we were trying to do. I took Gordon Murphy, the seaway's chief engineer, along with me. To our surprise, we encountered a somewhat cool reception. The meeting was being held in the old section of the village on top of a hill in a corrugated iron hall or arena. Into this arena were packed most of the village's Indians, and quite a few other people too, including representatives from the Montreal press.

I was a little annoyed at our reception and told one of the Indians' representatives, "I was invited to a friendly

105

private meeting, but this looks like a public meeting to me." But although the reporters and photographers waited expectantly nearby, they were disappointed. As the guest, I spoke to the meeting first and spent about half an hour explaining in detail all the plans of the Seaway Authority in the Caughnawaga reservation.

After my speech, someone rose to reply on behalf of the Indians. He claimed that the seaway could not take land from the people of Caughnawaga. The Iroquois of this village were members of the Six Nations who held their land by treaty with the British Government. Since the treaty was concluded before the British North America Act, Canada had no jurisdiction over these people or their land. This argument, although eloquently expressed, did not impress me. If there had been the faintest chance of a court upholding that point of view, we would have been forced to put the seaway on the other side of the river—at an additional cost of many millions.

It was also claimed that we were taking far more land than we needed. At this stage, the Indians decided to send the press away. I asked for the right of reply, which was granted. I told the meeting that the Authority had already done a great deal for the Indians. We had filled in some low-lying lands in the reservation so that they could be reclaimed; we were providing a water and sewage system; preserving old stone houses of sentimental value; building a wall to protect the Jesuit church; and were paying compensation equal to anything paid any white man along the river.

I can't estimate how persuasive I was, but the Indian chief then produced a pipe of peace, lit it, and passed it round among the principal dignitaries present. When it came to my turn, I took a good pull at it, but learned later to my chagrin that I had been smoking it upside down. I endured a great ribbing from my colleagues in the seaway the following morning when a picture featuring the upside-down pipe was published in a Montreal

106

newspaper. "You should be more careful," one colleague said. "One hundred years ago, we would never have left that meeting alive!"

Actually, it was the Quebec Government which had the legal responsibility of dealing with the Indians over their land. But the Seaway Authority was forced to negotiate with the Indians directly because Premier Duplessis would have nothing to do with the problem. This was astute politics. Why should he court needless unpopularity? Let the Seaway Authority and his old enemy the Federal Government do that.

In the subsequent legal negotiations, which delayed the seaway about six months at that point, all the cases brought against the Seaway Authority for injunctions to restrain us from proceeding were thrown out of court.

At Iroquois, the Authority had to expropriate about thirty to forty landowners. These men had farms at Iroquois Point where part of the land was being sliced away for the seaway channel. The majority of the farmers accepted the expropriation offers, but one man contested our offer because of peculiar circumstances. He had a valuable orchard in varying stages of development and his demands were so high that the case had to go to the Exchequer Court. As already mentioned, a separate valuation of each tree was made—and there were thousands of trees—before the case was settled to everybody's satisfaction.

MOVING OLD SETTLEMENTS

The problem of expropriation in the Cornwall-International Rapids section of the river was made difficult because of the old associations of many of the residents. The area is replete with history, some of which goes back hundreds of years. Before the flooding began at Cornwall I can remember a team of archaeologists working like Trojans on Sheek Island to dig up the last relics of an-

107

cient Indian remains dating back about 3,500 years. All this country was the heartland of the Iroquois.

The United Empire Loyalists followed the Mohawk trail in their escape from the Americans. When they arrived in the Cornwall area, they occupied the best of the land along the river. Later, Scotch Catholics joined them. Later still came French Canadians. It is said, perhaps apocryphally, that the Scots were placed between the other two groups as a buffer state. If there is any truth in it, there was no sign of it when I was a youngster. All the ethnic and religious groups got along well at Cornwall.

The immigrants of the eighteenth and nineteenth century to this area were solid citizens in search of the best place to live and die. They reared their children to fear the Lord, tend their land and take care of the old folks. The communities that grew up along the river bank such as Mille Roches, Moulinette, Wales, Dickinson's Landing, Farran's Point, Aultsville, Morrisburg and Iroquois had their roots deeply into the soil.

It was with this knowledge that the Ontario Hydro Electric Power Commission approached the unpleasant task of telling these people that not only were they to lose their land but that it was to be buried under sixty to seventy feet of water. The commission is experienced in acquiring land, but it had never had to do so on quite such a large scale. After eighteen months of examination and discussion, Hydro officials first went to the various churches in the area to be flooded. Through experience, they knew how easy it is for expropriation to be viewed emotionally at first, and they felt that by explaining their plans for the future to the leaders of the churches, they would be enlisting the support of the most influential members of the community for a start. They offered to move the churches bodily to new and larger sites. If it was not possible to move the churches, then Hydro would build new ones. Actually, the only church to make

108

Moving the People

the move was the 127-year-old Anglican Christ Church at Moulinette.

Of course the valley had known for many years that if the power development did go ahead, many farms would be lost through flooding. But few realized how widespread the flooding would be. After the churches, the Hydro men went to the municipalities with the same propositions. Most municipal offices were old and needed modernizing or repairing. The Hydro offer of new offices was attractive. Then it was publicly explained how the commission intended establishing three new towns by the shores of the future lake. These would be laid out on modern lines, with community centres, brand-new business sections, schools and churches.

Hydro was faced by roughly three types of person. There was the person who would accept cash and who would either rebuild nearby or move from the district. Second, there was the man who would demand to be resettled. Usually he was also reluctant to move from his house or give it up. Last, there was the man who did not want to move, or sell, or be resettled, or do anything but stay exactly where he was.

There were other people who could not be classified so easily. They were dealt with individually, perhaps emotionally. One 94-year-old woman was extremely reluctant to move, and she was allowed to stay in her house until the last moment.

Hydro felt it had the answer to the demands of every person to be deprived of his house or land. For those who would accept cash, there was little chance of argument. For those who wanted to be resettled, Hydro expropriated farmland near where the waters of the future lake would rise. The new towns were laid out near the relocated No. 2 Highway and the relocated double-track C.N.R. line. The towns were named Long Sault (160 acres), eight miles west of Cornwall, Ingleside (200 acres), 13 miles west of Cornwall, and New Iroquois, 30 miles west of Cornwall. The old village of

109

Iroquois moved its first house in the fall of 1955 and the last family moved in the fall of 1957 to the new location about a mile north. The largest community affected by the flooding was Morrisburg. Here, Hydro moved the southern part of the town to a new subdivision on the north of the community. Almost all the business section, more than 40 stores, had to be moved.

A house-moving contractor bodily moved several hundred houses from the valley to the new towns and villages. Two machines, capable of lifting up to 200 tons, were used. To move a house, the contractor built a steel frame under the sills and load-bearing portions of the building. The U-shaped machine, powered by a 200-horsepower engine, backed up to the building, electric winches were attached to the steel frame and the building was hoisted up till the frame rested on the machine. The building was then hauled to its new site where a new basement or foundations had been prepared to fit it. All kinds of structures could be moved this way, even ancient stone structures with crumbling mortar and cracked walls.

The house moving was featured in magazines, newspapers, radio and television programmes all over the world. The people of the valley coined many jokes describing their peculiar change in life. One story concerned a farmer who was a notoriously bad driver. "Hear about Jim?" the story went. "Knocked his porch off, backin' up." Another story had it that the provincial police were issuing $1,000 tickets for houses parked more than two hours.

When all the houses had been moved, the new towns looked strange. A visitor would be baffled for a moment trying to understand what was so different about them. Then he would realize that he was seeing rows of houses up to 70 to 100 years old laid out on post-war subdivision lines with modern concrete sidewalks, light poles and power lines.

110

During the all-out engineering surveys of the St. Lawrence during the fall of 1952, so many hydraulic problems were met that engineers felt we needed an enormous
model of the entire projected waterway if we were to accurately estimate the problems ahead. However, it trans-
pired that this could not be done with one model. The
length of the river was too great. It would be more con-
venient to have models of sections of the river close to
the section involved.

After we discussed the matter with the engineers of the
Ontario Hydro Electric Power Commission, the commission built three models of the river from Prescott down
to Cornwall. The Department of Transport built another
model which covered the river below that point to Lake
St. Francis.

I believe that these models, which were in operation
almost continuously from the time they were first built,
saved the seaway and power project millions of dollars.
The National Research Council built a scale model of a
lock on the Welland Canal, which had the exact proportions—80 feet wide, 766 feet long, with 30 feet of water
over the lock sills—of all the seaway locks we built. By
experimenting with this model, we found out exactly
how quickly we could lock a ship. The engineers also
were able to devise a specially fast method of filling and
emptying the lock and this probably paid for the cost of
the model alone. Eventually, after much experimenting,
they got the speed of lockage down to eight minutes.

The models helped us to deal with the problem of the
peculiarly high water-level of Lake Ontario during the
summer of 1952. This was blamed on the Gut Dam,
which Canada had constructed with U.S. agreement between 1903 and 1906 above the Galops Rapids between
Adams Island in Canada and Galop Island in the U.S.
It was built to compensate for channel enlargements

111

The Models

which had been carried out some time before by Canada in the channel north of Adams Island.

As the water in the lake rose steadily, there was alarm that lakeshore owners would soon be making damage claims—and these could be unbelievably high. Before the dam was removed in 1953, the National Research Council built a model of the areas above and below the dam and made exhaustive tests to see what effect the dam had had on the lake and what effect its removal would have. It was able to prove to the Federal Government's satisfaction that the dam was not responsible for the rising lake level and that the government should not accept responsibility for damage claims.

The models showed us quickly that one-third of the river flow went north of Cornwall Island, while two-thirds flowed on the south. They showed us all the peculiarities of currents in Montreal Harbour. They also showed us accurately the effects of any proposed dredging. They enabled us to devise balancing works where the dredging had thrown the river out of balance. They also enabled us to answer effectively any complaints that were made about possible damage to harbour works or operation as a result of our construction of the seaway.

The models repaid their investment costs many dozens of times over.

CHAPTER EIGHT

THE BATTLE OF THE TOLLS

The Question of Toll Rates

Surprise Over Welland

Practical Details

THE QUESTION OF TOLL RATES

If it were merely a matter of opening and closing locks, keeping them repaired, and ensuring a smooth flow of shipping, joint operation of the St. Lawrence Seaway would be easy. But, unhappily, nothing on the seaway is so simple. The seaway is a self-sustaining public utility, and it must, by international agreement, pay for itself in fifty years by collecting money from the people who use it.

There is a chance that if Canada had built the seaway alone, no tolls would be charged today, although it is a faint chance in view of the great costs. But the U.S. was adamant right from the start of final negotiations that the project must be "self-liquidating within a reasonable period". This set in motion some of the most complicated negotiations in the history of the seaway.

The question of tolls was often used as a political and economic argument to make the seaway impossible. The powerful interests in the U.S., when they could no longer stop the construction of the seaway, tried to get the tolls

114

pinned at hopelessly high rates, high enough to scare all shipping away from the seaway. Of course, users of the canals will never agree that tolls are absolutely necessary. Somehow we had to make them high enough to pay off our investment costs, but low enough to keep attracting ships.

When the toll charges were first announced in May, 1958, after years of negotiations, it was reported in newspapers that some large freighters would pay up to $12,000 to run the full length of the seaway.

The toll rates are, in my opinion, fair and reasonable when measured against the benefits and economies that the seaway provides. A 20,000-ton upper laker with a cargo of wheat—about 660,000 bushels—could be sent down the seaway for about $30,000 less than by the 14-foot canal system with its two trans-shipment points at Prescott and Montreal. Even if the toll did amount to,

115

The Question of Toll Rates

roughly, $10,000 on this cargo, the saving would still be $20,000.

It is interesting that the U.S. and Canada finally agreed that tolls should be charged, because the Canadian tradition has been against charging for canal use. This is probably almost a direct result of Canada's experience over the Erie Canal which played such havoc with Montreal's trade and Canadian canals in general.

As a result of Erie's operations from the middle of the last century, all tolls were abolished on the Welland Canal and tolls on all Canadian canals disappeared in 1905. Canals were accepted in the Canadian mind as a necessary expense on public moneys. It was with this approach that Canadian planners began dealing with the seaway.

They were not inhibited by the cost of the project. A glance at the record books shows Canada's willingness to spend liberally on waterways. For over fifty years, Canada has developed ports and harbours to offer shippers the finest and most efficient facilities. By 1953, as far as the records tell, Canada had spent more than one billion dollars on canals, harbours, the St. Lawrence ship channel, public works dredging, and other works.

How are tolls estimated?

An estimate is made of the capital cost and how much the seaway is going to cost annually to operate and maintain. This includes a second estimate of how many ships might enter the waterway and how much tonnage they might collectively carry. This is difficult to do accurately. There are many unknowns. How many tons of iron ore will be sent from the new Labrador resources to plants along the Great Lakes? How much American freight will find it cheaper to use the seaway than, say, the Mississippi, or the railroads to New York? Because the seaway now lets the huge inland ships, the lakers, down to Montreal, will they handle most of the freight with Montreal the main trans-shipment point, or will foreign vessels

116

take over much of this freight and ship it direct to its destination?

Because the seaway is a canal on which tolls are charged, there is a temptation to compare it with Panama and Suez. There is, of course, a close physical resemblance, but little economic relationship.

Both Panama and Suez provide ship routes that save thousands of miles over their nearest alternatives. At the same time, they *can* be by-passed. Ships that use them in one direction are not obliged to return by them. This situation is reflected in toll charges. For example, on the Panama Canal, unloaded vessels are charged 80 per cent of the toll of loaded ships.

The seaway lets the ships of the world into the heart of North America, but it is not a meeting-place of many different trade routes as are the other two canals. The seaway cannot form part of a triangular route which a ship can use only once before returning to its starting-point.

Another factor having an effect on the calculation of tolls is that the seaway is flanked by railways and highways. These routes compete on many classes of cargo. I like to think of the seaway as being a sort of toll highway. Just like such a highway, it offers certain advantages for the movement of traffic, provided these are not defeated by too restrictive a toll policy.

When parliament decided in 1951 to go ahead with the St. Lawrence Seaway and construct all the necessary navigation works to take 27-foot draught ships, provision was made for the imposition of tolls. However, in March, 1947, the question of tolls had been raised by the Americans. They have always been preoccupied by the fear that the seaway would become a public charge. Louis St. Laurent, then Secretary of State for External Affairs, told the House of Commons, "The Canadian Government had now concurred in principle with the proposal to make the St. Lawrence Seaway self-liquidat-

117

The Question of Toll Rates

ing by means of toll charges subject to making arrangements satisfactory to both Governments. . . ."

Almost exactly the same statement was made to the United States Government in 1951. Canada said she approved the principle of tolls but made no reference to the extent of the work to be paid for, or to the division of expenditures between the two countries, or to the allocation of costs between power and navigation.

When both Canada and the U.S. had agreed to build the seaway, their regulations covering toll collecting were a reflection of both countries' attitude towards the tolls problem. Canada's seaway legislation made it clear that the Authority may establish a tariff of tolls which shall be "fair and reasonable". The U.S. legislation directs the Corporation to reach an agreement with Canada or otherwise to impose tolls for the use of the facilities.

Yet despite all the complexities and headaches of the tolls problem, they helped to swing the U.S. into seaway construction. Soon after we had announced our decision to go ahead alone, President Eisenhower called for a delay of some months during which a last attempt would be made to have legislation approved by Congress. Canada reluctantly agreed.

An energetic senator, Alexander Wiley, long a believer in the seaway, worked hard preparing legislation and succeeded in getting the Senate's approval. One of the reasons for his success was the provision for the liquidation of the capital, maintenance and operating costs through tolls.

Senator Wiley prepared a "St. Lawrence Seaway Manual" which says, in part: "Although many of these advantages are assumed in any event, since Canada will build the Seaway alone if we fail to take advantage of the opportunity to participate, there are compelling economic reasons why United States participation is of the utmost importance.

"Only by such participation will we have a voice in the management and control of the seaway. The desir-

118

The Battle of the Tolls

ability of having a voice in such matters as construction standards, operating rules and regulations, standards of maintenance, and the setting of priorities for ships in transit is apparent, since the vessels using the waterway will be predominantly American flag vessels and the commerce will consist to a large degree of commodities either originating in or destined for the United States."

This is a point which worried Americans almost since the first day international co-operation was mentioned to build the seaway. Wiley emphasized that the U.S. must have a voice in setting tolls. She must be able to watch for the possibility of reducing tolls when possible. "Under sole Canadian control, however," he says, "there would seem to be every incentive to operate the project as a revenue producing investment, with the United States interests, in effect, continuing to pay rental for its use."

U.S. participation in the seaway was perhaps a foregone conclusion at any time we may have cared to say we were building the seaway alone. The U.S. could not permit Canada to dominate the seaway. For the same reason, she was loath to see Canada planning duplicate facilities during construction of the joint venture.

SURPRISE OVER WELLAND

Because Canada had completed the Welland Canal to a depth of twenty-five feet in 1932, many observers thought that the Welland would be outside the tolls problem. There was great surprise when Canada announced that the Welland would be included in the tolls programme—and not a little annoyance. Why, it was asked, should Canada seek to make a profit out of something that was already paid for by public money?

However, Canada has always stated that if money was spent on the Welland to complete the seaway, it would be chargeable to the seaway account. The latest agreement between Canada and the United States in 1941,

119

which never became operative, recognized this fact. Canada does not want to recapture the capital cost of the Welland. But to dredge the canal to 27 feet cost us about $30 million, and it will cost about another $2 million a year to run it. Any ship-owner who complains about having to pay Welland tolls should remember that they are calculated on the additional, not capital, cost.

PRACTICAL DETAILS

Both the Canadian Authority and the U.S. Corporation established toll committees, which worked for years trying to reach fair toll rates. This was a difficult task. The credit for much of the success of this work goes to Jean Lessard, vice-president of the Seaway Authority and Reece Harrill, his opposite number on the U.S. Corporation. Lessard is one of the most competent men I know in the public service.

The committees had to answer many questions such as "Why not charge a flat fee for all ships, as for a ride on subway or streetcar?" The answer is that there is a tremendous difference in the size of the ships and the cargoes they carry. The biggest ship using the seaway can take 25,000 tons of cargo. The smallest ships take less than 3,000 tons. To impose a flat rate toll would keep out all ships except the very largest. The idea is further unacceptable because the operation costs of the seaway will be a tiny portion of the total amount to be paid back.

However, although it is agreed that a bigger ship with a bigger cargo must pay more to use the channel, this ship must not pay more per ton than a small ship. During discussions on whether tolls should be based on deadweight tonnage, net registered tonnage, ship length, cargo tonnage, or other factors, it was found very easy to create discriminatory tolls which would make it more expensive for a big ship to carry a ton of textiles to Toronto than a small ship.

120

The Battle of the Tolls

While the committees worked away, some public questions were being asked. "How," it was asked, "would tolls affect various commodities? Will certain commodities or certain classes of traffic receive more favourable rates than others? In other words, will the seaway toll system be used like another type of tariff? Will there be any discrimination in tolls between Canadian and American traffic or between local and overseas traffic?"

The public need not have worried. The tolls committees were highly sensitive to the great dangers of discrimination. A Canadian committee member once said to me, "Our aim is no discrimination, achieved through the greatest simplicity which human ingenuity can devise."

But the tolls committees, however clear their intentions, faced difficulties in determining the classifications of products. How much of the traffic on the seaway, they had to ask themselves, would consist of bulk commodities such as iron ore, grain or coal, all of which could move in the largest ships at full capacity? How much would consist of other bulk or semi-bulk commodities such as pulpwood, salt, or wood-pulp, which ordinarily is not moved in lots large enough for bulk carriers? If these products continued to move in the medium and smaller type of ships, what effect would this have? How much finally would consist of general merchandise or package freight which moves in the smallest lots on regularly scheduled ships?

While all these questions had to be answered as accurately as possible, the tolls committees were helped by one thing. It was known that a great percentage of seaway traffic would consist of bulk traffic of two products—iron ore going upstream from Labrador and grain going downstream from the west. This, it was estimated, would account for 70 per cent of the seaway's traffic.

On the remaining traffic, the committees faced the temptations of charging separate rates for separate products. This would raise a lot of money. It could be made

121

Practical Details

acceptable to consigners. However, it would only be a justifiable temptation if the volume of traffic was so low that enough money could not be collected to pay for the project.

This brings us to the history of estimates of tonnage likely to use the new channel. In 1954, the St. Lawrence Seaway Development Corporation estimated that available traffic would be 36½ million tons for 1959 and 52 million tons for 1963. This was an official estimate, the last one to be made by the U.S. It replaced all other previous guesses made variously by the Department of Commerce or the Corps of Engineers between 1931 and 1951.

In Canada, a very detailed estimate was made by the Department of Trade and Commerce in the early 1940s which anticipated 44½ million tons annually, five years after the opening of the seaway. In one speech made while I was president of the Authority, I predicted 30 to 35 million tons during the first five years of operation, a prediction made after careful study by Seaway Authority economists.

Rising costs made toll estimation difficult. During the four-year period that the seaway was being built, costs rose each year. At one stage, it was thought the navigation part of the seaway would cost a little more than $300 million. By the time construction was over, this figure was well over $400 million.

But if the foregoing difficulties are forbidding, there are worse to come. There are, for a start, two types of tonnage, vessel tonnage and cargo tonnage. In cargo tonnage, there are two separate classes, weight and measurement. In the weight class, the ton might be 2,000 pounds (the short ton), 2,204.62 pounds (the metric ton) or 2,240 pounds (the long ton). Cargo measurement is generally standard at 100 cubic feet to the ton.

There are, unhappily for the tolls committees, four different systems for assessing gross and net tonnage for estimating port charges and canal tolls.

122

1. 1938 Oslo rules: These fix percentages of ballast that can be carried without charge by the ship.

2. U.S. rules and Panama Canal admeasurement rules, which permit unlimited ballasting required for the safety of ships.

3. National registry of gross and net tonnage by each country—or at the port at which the ship is registered.

4. Suez and Panama Canal Regulations which generally speaking are more strict than the national registration of gross and net tonnage.

The complicated picture presented by the tolls problem is fortunately clarified a lot by one simple truth. The bulk traffic will be the backbone of the seaway. On this traffic will swing nearly all the decisions on tolls and operation. A slight decrease in tolls on bulk traffic, for instance, would have to be compensated for by a considerable increase in tolls on the higher grade traffic, because of the great differences in tonnages of these two main classes of traffic.

Tolls are a system of taxation. Like personal taxation, they can be manipulated in many ways. If the rich people in a community are numerous enough, a steep increase in their taxes might make it possible to reduce taxes on the rest of the community. If the rich are not numerous, then the average resident must bear the brunt of the taxation.

The rich people are related, in the seaway, to bulk traffic. If the bulk traffic is enormous, sustained and essential, it will pay for most of the seaway. It will make possible low freight rates on packaged goods, encourage cross-country seaway freight on many items that might normally go by rail or truck. But if the bulk traffic is low, freight costs for other goods on the seaway could be impossibly high.

During the earliest discussions on tolls, the Americans were insistent that they should collect them for both countries. Lewis Castle wanted to collect them at Massena. The American point of view was that the U.S.

123

should collect them because it would be mostly American money, anyway.

But we were equally insistent that we must collect the tolls. Once, when discussions became a trifle heated, we had to point out that it would be difficult for the Americans to collect tolls after we had already collected them at Montreal. The Americans said they would collect tolls on downbound ships. We said we would collect downbound tolls at Welland, if necessary. This was not a serious argument, however. Nobody can deny that Canada should collect the tolls because the seaway begins and ends in Canadian territory.

Details of ships' cargoes are noted at Montreal and telephoned to Cornwall, the seaway headquarters. The bill is prepared and posted at Cornwall to the shipowners. When the bill is paid, two-thirds is paid into the Canadian seaway account, and one-third is sent to the U.S. The seaway will be debt free by 2008.

124

The Battle of the Tolls

CHAPTER NINE

EFFECTS OF THE SEAWAY

Old Anxieties

A Glimpse of the Future

Montreal's Reaction

St. Lawrence Traffic Jam?

OLD ANXIETIES

The possible effects of the seaway have frightened many
people. During the 1930s, it was predicted that construction of the seaway would destroy many industries,
perhaps bankrupt the railways. In those depression years,
business and commerce were far from normal. National
income in the U.S. which had been $87.4 billion in 1929
was down to less than half that in 1932. Nearly one
able-bodied man in four across North America was looking for work. There was cynicism and disbelief in the
established order of things.

It is not surprising that the industrialists were terrified
that a build-up of industry along the Great Lakes—
which completion of the seaway seemed to ensure—
would draw industry already established elsewhere. It is
easy to see the viewpoint of the seaboard ports of the
U.S. which argued that any plan "to let the ocean into
North America" would surely impoverish them. They
had little enough to live on then without seeing pieces of

126

their livelihood being given to the St. Lawrence Seaway. "Such a plan," said one U.S. politician of that time, referring to the seaway, "would make it relatively easy, as I understand it, for Canada to seize control of a section of the United States' northern frontier."

Both the railroads, and much eastern business were against the seaway. There were fears that if a shift of business did occur it would upset the entire economy of the east coast. Even the coal-miners were against it, on the ground that seaway traffic would cut down rail traffic. This would reduce the amount of coal that was necessary and cut down the number of coal miners needed. Anyone who visited the Pennsylvania coal-fields during the depression might feel sympathy for their fears. In ramshackle homes, thousands of miners struggled for life on diets of weed roots and dandelions.

Finally, of course, the coal and oil companies were vociferously opposed to the seaway. They feared it would

127

Old Anxieties

create a superabundance of cheap, state-produced power which would hurt their own businesses. A report of the Committee on Public Works of the House of Representatives indicates the feeling of those times: "The waterway would definitely harm the railroads, the Atlantic and Gulf ports, the coal industry, the independent oil producers, the American merchant marine and labor serving all of those industries and localities, while it would help primarily, five steel companies, one ore company, the port of Montreal and foreign vessel owners."

Nearly thirty years passed, but the opposition to the seaway did not change its character much. Gregory S. Prince, representing the rail carriers, told the Chicago Bar Association in 1957 that the crux of the rail argument against the seaway was that it was subsidized competition. He predicted that the canal would never pay for itself and that this would prompt its proponents to say, "You should double the size of the Welland Canal by putting in parallel locks. Then you will be able to liquidate the project."

Prince said that the goal would always be the same— to deepen the channel to take bigger ships so that the project would pay for itself—but the goal would always be just beyond reach. "Let me say," he said, "that until such time as the tolls levied can meet the economic charges of the seaway there can be no savings to be shared in by shippers using the waterway. They are entitled to no windfall at the expense of the taxpayers who have supplied the money for this investment and it will be our endeavour to sustain this point."

A GLIMPSE OF THE FUTURE

I do not think that anybody truly knows the full effects of the seaway on the Canadian and U.S. economies. We can only guess and try to remember some of the effects that the St. Lawrence has had on our country in years

128

Effects of the Seaway

past. We can recall again the tremendous impact that the opening of the Erie Canal had on Canada from 1825 onwards. The seaway has been compared with Erie. The effects may be equally startling.

The future of the seaway is related to the St. Lawrence's past history. It has been a history of continuous growth, vast change, major upsets. There was no holding back the seaway once Upper Canada was heavily settled and once the country felt the impact of thousands of immigrants pouring across the Atlantic to escape European depressions from the Battle of Waterloo through to the middle of the nineteenth century. They poured up the river—50,000 between 1815 and 1825, 28,000 in 1830 and 50,000 in 1831. They were human flotsam and jetsam, mostly penniless, many sick, but all hopeful. The St. Lawrence was their grand highway to freedom.

But the migrants found a churlish country waiting for them. Cholera swept through them as they huddled together at reception points on St. Lawrence islands. Those who escaped found a strange contrast between the broad expansive sweep of the beautiful river and the evil-smelling hovels into which they were packed. But the immigrants forged up the river, by steamboat and stage coach. They doubled the population of Upper Canada from 177,174 in 1827 to 321,145 in 1834.

They hastened the urgency of the seaway. By 1841, a nine-foot canalled channel was complete from Montreal to Lake Ontario. Today's migrants, sailing comfortably upstream as far as Quebec or Montreal in their air-conditioned liners, to their destination in all parts of Canada, could reflect on the good fortune that brought them here in the twentieth century instead of 100 years ago.

To try to predict the future of the seaway may be a difficult task, but it is also an exciting one. It is exciting to reflect how wrong were those people who predicted that the Erie Canal would finish the St. Lawrence waterway. It is exciting to think back to the coming of the railroads and how they affected the St. Lawrence. It is

129

A Glimpse of the Future

interesting to note how advances in one form of transport more often than not opened new opportunities for others. The railways gave superior service and speed, but they pointed to the modern use of the seaway as a bulk carrier.

When the railways broke through the barrier of the Precambrian Shield, they created a new source for lake traffic from the west. It was the railways that made possible the opening of the west for the large-scale production of grain. It was the Great Lakes route which made it possible for western grain to reach overseas markets at competitive prices.

If any hard and fast prediction can be made about the future of the seaway it is probably this: Iron ore and wheat will be the backbone of the waterway. In fact, the discovery of iron ore in vast quantities in Labrador hastened the building of the seaway. It was one of the influences that helped Canada make up her mind to go ahead alone if necessary. It helped to balance the continental freight position. There was a linking of rail and water transport in 1854 with the opening up of the vast iron ore ranges of northern Michigan and Minnesota. From the first, the huge lake transports were the vital link between the fields of ore and the steel mills in Ohio and Pennsylvania. But they were a weak link. Their existence depended on steel mills and ore-fields being close to water. When the giant Mesabi iron range began running out, the shipping pattern of the Great Lakes was changed forever. There were grave fears that the bulk ore-shipping business would disappear. The great ships, specifically built for carrying ore, would languish in their inland sea. The discovery of ore in Labrador saved the day.

The grain traffic on the Great Lakes, however, was quite different. It had to go right down the river. The big lakers took the grain to the trans-shipment elevators at Prescott at the head of the St. Lawrence canals, the canallers took it to Montreal.

With such a pressure of pent-up traffic in the Great

130

Lakes wanting to find the easiest route to the sea, it seems strange that the seaway was not built long ago. But it has always been a tremendous project, much more than a few million dollars. During the depression, the high cost was sufficient to stall construction. Building it before World War II would have had serious effects on other forms of transport. Rail freights were already at disastrously low levels. The seaway was too big then.

Immigration waves doubled the population of Upper Canada in less than ten years midway through the last century. After World War II, the great increase in population in the U.S. and Canada finally made the seaway not only possible but essential. From 1939 to 1954, while the seaway project remained the same size, the U.S. increased its population by one-third and Canada by one-half. The gross national products of both countries trebled. The potential steel-making capacity of Canada was multiplied three times. Steel production increased twice in the U.S. and eight times in Canada. Five hundred per cent more electric power was produced in Canada.

Canada is still in the middle of a period of intense economic development. It is this development which helped make the seaway a reality and will make its future brilliant. This development will undoubtedly quickly overtax its single channel, bringing trade and wealth to everything it touches. The U.S. steel industry has predicted that within the next fifteen years, there will be a 60-million-ton increase in steel-making capacity in the U.S. The additional ore requirements for such an increase dwarfs the potential normal output of the Quebec-Labrador mines.

In addition, not only will the seaway directly reduce the transport costs to consumer and industry, but it will also have wide general effects. Certain industries will follow the seaway to find fuels, such as coal or oil, or basic raw materials, more cheaply. Some industries may need raw materials or semi-manufactured goods which

131

are not dependent on low-cost movement. Accordingly, there will be a traffic interchange, with some industries replacing others, resulting in a ceaseless and dynamic interflow of industry along the St. Lawrence Seaway.

But this does not mean that the Great Lakes will benefit from the seaway to the exclusion of all other regions. In fact, it is more likely that areas near the seaway will act as a spark plug for the development of more industry considerable distances away.

MONTREAL'S REACTION

Montreal has always been the most sensitive city to the future possibilities of the seaway. It reacted strongly to its construction. By the end of 1958, a $65-million construction project was under way in its harbour, including new grain elevators, wharves, piers and sheds.

The city has difficulty in forgetting what happened to Quebec when Montreal began developing as a port. Many of its citizens feared that what happened to Quebec could easily happen to Montreal if Toronto really tried to take the trade away. Although it is unthinkable today that Montreal could decline as a world port, seaway or no seaway, there persists in the city a vague feeling that the heart of Canada is moving steadily west and that the seaway will hasten that move.

This feeling may be partially true, but to assume that it will hurt Montreal is nonsense. Montreal will earn more, not less, business. Shipping companies have plans for their ships to bring ore from the east, clean ship, then return to the coast with grain. In such a scheme, Montreal will become an even greater trans-shipment point than it is now. In 1956, 2,600,000 tons of ore moved up the old St. Lawrence canals for the Great Lakes. The seaway should take at least 10,000,000 tons of ore right from the beginning. In fact, the province of Quebec itself may one day become a great steel producer. Already

132

Effects of the Seaway

a steel industry has established itself in that great industrial triangle which extends from Valleyfield to Sorel, with Montreal as the focal point.

The example of Montreal's south shore shows how business men are aware of the possibilities of the seaway. When we were first planning the channel along the south shore, we learned that land speculation was rife along the shoreline. Some properties changed hands half a dozen times in a year, each time for a higher price. This occurred before it had been positively announced that the seaway would be built. When we did begin construction, the channel plans included provision for a number of large turning basins dug south of the channel. These would permit ships to unload along the south shore and turn for their trip back overseas. By the time the seaway was nearly finished, this land boom had blossomed into what amounted to an unbuilt industrial complex at the doorstep of down-town Montreal. There is 200 square miles of available land for development from the south shore to the U.S. border. It will be this land, say the experts, which permits Montreal to boost its population to three million by 1985. Montreal's position will be tremendously enhanced by the seaway.

Elsewhere along the St. Lawrence, the effects of the seaway have been impressive already. From Quebec to Duluth-Superior, a distance of more than 2,000 miles, every town, village and city along the waterway has plans to expand with the seaway. One of the first cities to react to the seaway was Duluth-Superior. When seaway construction was begun, the ports there began deepening harbours, building new docks and preparing publicity campaigns to get new business. At Milwaukee, a five-year five-million-dollar harbour improvement plan went into operation. At Chicago, planners proposed to spend nearly $30 million on harbour improvements in the belief that the city would become a world port when the seaway was finished. Toledo, Erie's busiest port, considered a $20-million cargo terminal. Buffalo spent

133

$50,000 on an economic and physical survey of its port, with tentative plans to spend nearly $6 million on port improvements. Oswego hired a port director and called for a port survey.

In Canada, the effects of seaway construction were slower to take hold. But as construction went ahead, so did the ports. The Lakehead—Port Arthur and Fort William—planned a new cargo terminal and dredging; Windsor predicted a huge increase in its shipping business even though it already is situated on the busiest waterway in the world, the Detroit River. Cornwall bought 113 acres for harbour development. Sarnia, whose harbour is not a paying proposition, was hopeful that the seaway might help out. Kingston, which for a quarter of a century has been the main service point for mid-St. Lawrence traffic, was pessimistic about the seaway because no dredging had been done to allow ocean-going ships into its harbour. But if it could get the dredging done, it expected a boom. The general manager of the Toronto Harbour Commissioners, Ernest B. Griffith, announced a $7-million port expansion plan towards the end of 1958. Hamilton, Canada's third busiest port with rapidly increasing freight tonnages handled each year, looked forward to a huge increase in business.

The seaway will affect every part of Canada. When I was introducing the seaway bill to the House of Commons, some of my colleagues were reluctant to support it. They could see no direct benefit to their constituents. They supported it because it was to benefit Canada as a whole. This must indirectly help everybody in the country, as one colleague said to me.

Specifically, I believe the seaway will have these effects on Canada. It will not hurt the fortunes of the railways, despite the complaints in the past from the U.S. Almost half the expected seaway traffic will be iron ore from Seven Islands, Quebec. This will be all new traffic which the railways could not have looked forward to anyway. Another large part of the expected freight will

134

Effects of the Seaway

be grain and coal which already uses the water route for much of its travelling. The great industrial development that the seaway will help may be expected to give the railways new and high-class traffic.

Despite the fears of some of my political colleagues, the seaway will not hurt the Maritimes. It will give a cheaper exchange route for all Maritime goods. It will open up new movements between the Atlantic provinces and all the Canadian ports in the Great Lakes. Potatoes, pulpwood, lumber and sugar will come from the east in increasing quantities. The seaway will help the Maritimes send their lumber to the U.S. Frozen fish from the Maritimes could penetrate the middle west via the seaway.

Ontario, already equipped with a kind of Canadian Ruhr along its lake-shore, will feel the effects of the seaway from every possible direction. Reserves of cheap power will help to build up industry, keep costs down. Dozens of lakeside towns are in excellent positions, by developing deep-water facilities, to attract industry. Ontario's industrial build-up will quicken.

For the prairies, the effects of the seaway are harder to predict. But for all grain normally shipped through the Great Lakes to Montreal, there will be big savings in the direct shipment now possible through the seaway. And for British Columbia, the seaway should help the marketing of lumber in the Great Lakes area.

ST. LAWRENCE TRAFFIC JAM?

A seaway is like a roadway. Both carry traffic and both are limited to how much they can carry. If the St. Lawrence seaway is to operate effectively it must avoid traffic jams.

Long before the seaway was built, it was estimated that about 30 to 35 million tons of cargo would go up and down the channel every year. About 60 per cent of this, it was estimated, would be new traffic volume in the

135

form of grain and iron ore movements. Leading secondary items would consist of petroleum products, coal, coke and forest products, accounting for 25 per cent of the total.

In 1950, the Department of Trade and Commerce calculated that 32.5 million tons of freight would move yearly on the seaway and it is interesting to compare this estimate with the Welland Ship Canal movements. In 1955, the Welland carried 20.9 million tons, of which 4.3 million was upbound and 16.6 million downbound. This imbalance meant that the Welland has never operated close to its real capacity. Its real capacity depends on the ships using it, of course, but we may quickly determine its capacity under widely varying conditions.

The length of the navigation season averages 240 days, and 14 lockages a day in each direction are easily handled by the canal. Theoretically then, 3,360 lockages are possible each season in each direction. However, traffic is not so uniform, so we should regard 3,000 lockages as being a more reasonable figure. If upbound and downbound traffic is reasonably balanced, then we can quickly calculate some total capacity figures based on the average size of ships using the canal. For instance:

Average tonnage of cargo per vessel	Total capacity of canal per year
5,000	30,000,000
6,000	36,000,000
7,000	42,000,000
8,000	48,000,000
9,000	54,000,000
10,000	60,000,000

The practical capacity of the Welland Ship Canal is somewhere between 50 and 60 million tons a year. The average cargo tonnage would be probably between nine and ten thousand tons with some empty movements in both directions.

This figure of 60 million tons, when compared with

136

the pre-seaway tonnage carried by the Welland of 20 million tons, may seem to be an extremely large figure, but it is not. It is dwarfed by the tonnage carried through the locks of the Sault Ste. Marie canals. In 1955, the Sault canals took 114,000,000 tons, including 89,000,000 tons of iron ore. In that same year, the St. Lawrence canals took 11,000,000 tons. The difference between the three systems of canals was that the Sault canals are double track—one on the American side and one on the Canadian. The Welland is partially doubled and the St. Lawrence canals were all single channel.

The immense bulk of tonnage taken by the Sault canals is a good guide as to what might happen to the St. Lawrence in terms of gross tonnage a few years in the future. When more than 100,000,000 tons are being hoisted up and down the St. Lawrence every year, we may see the greatest complex of industry the world has ever seen lining the banks of the St. Lawrence and the Great Lakes.

At the moment, most industry is along the Great Lakes. Most tonnage carried is from lake to lake. In the season of 1955, the lake carriers moved 194 million tons of cargo in four bulk items alone. This volume, reported by the Lake Carriers Association, included 101 million tons of iron ore, 53 million tons of coal, 29 million tons of limestone and 11 million tons of grain. Most of this traffic was United States tonnage, but they are interesting figures to compare with the 1955 Canadian railways figure of 168 million tons of revenue freight of all kinds, carried from coast to coast.

The impact of the seaway will be heavy on this trade. By that, I do not mean there will be serious disruptions of the present methods of transportation—such as foreign tonnage taking over a good deal of the pre-seaway freight. I mean that the seaway will cause such a change in the industrial set-up along the shores of the lakes that the patterns of transportation will be forced to change radically. The total volume of material carried will rise

137

sharply as the freight starts pouring up and down the St. Lawrence Seaway.

The seaway could not have been built at a more fortunate time. The hopes of more than a century that it would become the main trade route between the middle west and Europe have now come true. For the first time in history, the people of the middle western states can regard the St. Lawrence as their main outlet to the markets of the world. The people of Europe may regard Montreal and Toronto as the largest ports on Canada's south coast, Chicago the biggest on the U.S. north shore.

The seaway is not the final development of the St. Lawrence route. Bigger developments lie ahead. But the building of the seaway is so far the most exciting chapter in the St. Lawrence story.

138

Effects of the Seaway

CHAPTER TEN

THE EIGHTH SEA

Looking Back

Achievement at Last

LOOKING BACK

The history of the St. Lawrence and the fight for the seaway has been a history of ships. Basically it has been a battle to get bigger and bigger ships up the river, to move heavier and heavier cargoes. Now that the seaway is complete, an epoch is ended. The old dream of the pioneers has been realized. The ocean has been let into the North American heartland.

Looking at the seaway now with its gigantic locks, power-houses, dams, enormous channels cut across fields, islands, cities, with its 20,000-ton ships steaming majestically up and down the river, it is interesting to note the changes that two and a half centuries have brought to the great waterway. The ships have replaced the muscular and colourful voyageurs, heaving and straining their canoes overland past the rapids, watching for Iroquois, and dreaming of a fortune in furs from the hinterland. They have replaced the soldiers and the raft men.

This was first the fur highway, claiming the title

140

from the Ottawa River towards the end of the eighteenth century. But fur quickly gave way to more prosaic freight, like wheat and flour. By 1791, Kingston was a substantial trans-shipment point for thousands of bushels of wheat bound for export to Spain and England. When England went to war with France, this wheat became vital. Nearly 400,000 bushels of wheat was convoyed to England by H.M.S. *Envoy*, an English warship, in 1795. The destiny of the St. Lawrence Seaway was fixed then and the drive was on to build bigger ships, get merchandise up and down the river cheaper and faster.

The first small canals—pathetic affairs often less than a couple of feet deep with stone lock gates—took the bateaux, the small flat-bottomed boats that could carry two to four tons of freight. The canals and the bateaux quickly gave way to the Durham boats which first made their appearance towards the beginning of the nineteenth century, lugging their ten tons of freight along the river

141

with a maximum of utility and a minimum of grace or beauty. They jammed the warehouses of Montreal and Quebec with lumber, biscuit, flour, beef, pork and wheat. It was really little wonder that the merchants there became convinced that their two cities might become the greatest eastern seaboard ports.

The ships and boats along the waterway set the pace, with the canals stumbling along behind them. The canals were never quite big enough. It was always just a little too much money to spend to let the bigger ships up the waterway. By the time the bigger canals were built, there were bigger ships.

The first steamboat on the river was the *Accommodation*, owned by John Molson, which plied between Montreal and Quebec. She was quickly followed by others, some of them built above the rapids and never able to go down the river.

As the steamboats snorted up and down the river, it seemed there never would be canals to carry them. Dollier de Casson's dream of a canal at Lachine was only a dream and he had been dead more than a hundred years. Raft men brought freight down the Lachine Rapids and sometimes died there. A Captain Samuel Romilly of the Royal Engineers once prepared a comprehensive report on how a canal could be built at Lachine to take Durham boats. But the Imperial Government was so anxious about the danger of the Americans capturing Canada that it decided to build the Rideau Canal instead. Canada's canals should be kept as far as possible from the border where marauding Americans could easily cut water supply lines.

That was 140 years ago.

ACHIEVEMENT AT LAST

Today, there has been a vast change. The Americans still want to invade but they come peacefully. As tourists,

142

The Eighth Sea

they are spending millions of dollars about the sites of previous wars between our two countries along the St. Lawrence Valley. In our alterations to the river we have preserved reminders of the past. From Kingston down the river through the Thousand Islands, the big ships from all over the world steam steadily past a hundred battlefields, past islands where cunning *coureurs de bois* waited to fire one shot and see a canoe tip over far out on the river, where the pirate Bill Johnston sent a blazing ship floating downstream.

From Iroquois, it is almost as though we have created another thousand islands section but here the history had to be carefully preserved. The forty-mile lake is dotted with islands, most of them converted into parkland. Towards the left bank, a row of islands flanks the newly created towns of Ingleside, New Iroquois and Long Sault. A causeway links many of these islands and cars drive on them amidst the green of the parkland and the sparkling blue of the lake. These islands, and the land behind them, are part of Canada's greatest system of public parks. They were created with the seaway. In 1955, the Ontario Government set up the Ontario-St. Lawrence Development Commission to preserve historical associations in the St. Lawrence Valley and to create a vast vacation area. The New York Parks Commission did much the same thing on the other side of the river.

The development commission plans thousands of acres of parkland eventually. The centre of the initial development is the 2,000-acre Crysler Park, east of Morrisburg. It commemorates the victory of British and Canadian troops over the Americans in 1813 at the bloody battle of Crysler's Farm. Part of the farm now lies under the waters of the lake, but the war memorial has been moved. Cook's Tavern, an historic old stone building which was used by the American forces as a headquarters, was also successfully moved.

All the older buildings that were movable from the valley were assembled into Upper Canada Village, a re-

143

creation of United Empire Loyalist life. There is to be a tavern, coach house and stables, a church, pastor's house, a typical shop, blacksmith's shop, doctor's office, school, manor house, farm house, windmill, gun battery.

Preserving the ancient monuments has been a good thing for the valley because it has refocused attention on their importance and relation to the present. It drew attention, for instance, to Chimney Island, a scrap of land situated at the head of the old Galops Rapids about five miles west of Cardinal. This island was, according to the president of the Leeds and Grenville Historical Society, Lieutenant-Colonel F. C. Curry, the site of one of the last battles between France and England for dominion in North America.

Dredges working for the Authority had to dig out the ground nearly all round the tiny island which stands almost squarely in midstream. From a passing ship, the vaguest outlines can still be seen of the ancient French fortifications which crumbled under the combined weight of a powerful British army and ended French hopes of owning territory in Canada.

The French had fortified the island because it was one of the few spots on the river where a canoe could not pass without being seen. Soon after the capture of Quebec and the fall of Niagara, General Jeffrey Amherst began gathering a big army at Oswego to come down the St. Lawrence and storm Montreal, the centre of French resistance. Amherst arrived at the island, then called Fort de Levis, with 8,000 men. Opposing him was a garrison of 200 under Captain François Pouchot. Pouchot and his men held off the 8,000 for nearly a week, then surrendered with all his officers wounded and his ammunition gone. Amherst destroyed the fort and moved on, only to meet disaster himself in the Lachine Rapids when eighty-six of his men drowned in a mass upset of boats. While bombarding Fort de Levis, he used thirteen-inch mortar shells. Some cannon balls of this size were found when the Long Sault Rapids were drained. Lt.-Col. Curry

144

The Eighth Sea

feels that Amherst may have jettisoned them on his hasty way to Montreal.

On the southern side of the power-house lake, the Americans have created the St. Lawrence State Park. They had miles of dyking to construct for their section of the power and navigation project. They realized that this dyking would be an eyesore. During construction, they carefully stripped all topsoil from the excavation areas, and stockpiled it. When building was finished, they spread the soil over the raw scars left by the scrapers, bulldozers and drag-lines. On this soil, grass and trees were sown. In some areas, new forests were created. Two handsome beaches were built. The parklands stretch for thousands of acres south of the river.

East of this park area, the river is basically unchanged till Beauharnois, at the foot of Lake St. Francis. The seaway channel passes through the locks at the great power-house, crosses Lake St. Louis and begins to cut overland past the Lachine Rapids, swooping round the south shore of Montreal on the left, the developing south shore on the right. Steel skeletons of dozens of new industries can be seen. The sixteen-mile channel passes under the two down-town Montreal bridges and is finally released into the river.

Although my appointment as president of the St. Lawrence Seaway Authority had an initial term of ten years, I resigned the position after three. I was sorry to leave, but politics has a strange influence on one. It is in your blood. When Prime Minister St. Laurent invited me to return to the cabinet, I readily accepted. The Liberal Party was defeated at the 1957 general election.

I was re-elected to the House of Commons as a member of a sadly depleted party, now in Opposition.

The planning, designing and building of the seaway presented many people with broad and varied challenges in technique, organization and management. It showed the world a peculiar example of international and inter-provincial co-operation and good will. From those con-

145

Achievement at Last

ference rooms where we argued I have still a warm appreciation of the honesty and capability of the men I dealt with.

The U.S. and Canada are truly fortunate countries. Not only have we vast natural resources but nature has given us great rivers and streams surging with undeveloped waterpower. The St. Lawrence Seaway, with its locks and its power, is one of the major continuing themes of Canadian development. The river has for long been a channel along which we sent exports to Europe and brought imports back. The river has been an axis of our economy. Whenever the pull of the United States market has become strong enough to threaten our economic unity, we have reinforced this east-west axis—first by canals, later by railways. We have always had to fight the divisive north-south pull of the United States. In a sense, the construction of the St. Lawrence Seaway is a continuation of this national policy. But where before the river carried Canadian foodstuffs and raw materials for Europe, now a large part of the traffic will be raw materials for the United States. The St. Lawrence River, traditionally a symbol of Canada's origins in Europe, now is beginning to strengthen our ties with the United States.

As President Eisenhower said to me, we think alike, talk alike and behave alike. But instead of Canada being absorbed into the U.S., we are becoming momently more distinct and more sure of ourselves. The St. Lawrence Seaway showed us that, almost without knowing it, we had become a great power.

146

The Eighth Sea

INDEX

Accommodation, steamer, 142
"Act respecting the Construction of Works for the Generation of Electric Power in the International Rapids Section of the St. Lawrence River", 46
Adams Island, 111, 112
Allegheny Mountains, 24
Amherst, General Jeffrey, 11, 144, 145
Anderson, Robert B., 61
Aultsville, 108

Baltic and International Maritime Conference, 48
Barnhart Island, 95, 97
Beauharnois, 73, 74
Beauharnois Light, Heat and Power Company, 36, 92, 93
Beauharnois Power Canal, 11, 26, 93
Bersimis River, 34
Beston, Henry, 10
Bethlehem Steel, 18
Blackmore, J. H., 48
Bowden, W. A., 31, 32, 40
British Columbia, 135
British North America Act, 106
Brockville, 98
Brucker, Wilbur, 61, 75
Buffalo, 23, 133
Burpee, Lawrence, 70, 90

Calvin, D. D., 12
Canadian Cottons Ltd., 63
Canadian Industries Limited, 99
Canadian National Railways, 67, 68, 69, 109
Canadian Pacific Railways, 70, 71, 91
Canal de la Chine, *see* Lachine Canal

Cantin, Narcisse, 16, 17, 18, 19, 31
Cardinal, 144
Cartier, Jacques, 12, 15
Casson, Dollier de, 14, 16, 17, 19, 20, 31, 85, 142
Castle, Lewis G., 55, 58, 59, 60, 61, 77, 78, 123
Caughnawaga, 86, 91, 104, 105, 106
Challies, George, 29, 46, 55
Chicago, 6, 133, 138
Chimney Island, 144
Clinton, Governor De Witt, 23
Coldwell, M. J., 48
Cook's Tavern, 143
Cornwall, 2, 4, 5, 11, 16, 17, 28, 31, 39, 43, 44, 47, 55, 60, 63, 64, 65, 74, 75, 77, 94, 95, 107, 108, 109, 111, 124, 134
Cornwall Bridge, 71
Cornwall Canal, 2, 26, 27
Cornwall Island, 62, 74, 75, 77, 112
Côté, Ernest, 61
Côte Ste. Catherine, 86, 89, 91
Creighton, D. G., 24
Crysler Park, 143
Crysler's Farm, 143
Curry, Lt.-Col. F. C., 144

Detroit, 17, 27
Detroit River, 7, 134
Dewey, Thomas E., 55
Dickinson's Landing, 108
Dominion Bridge Ltd., 66, 87
Drew, George A., 48
Dulles, John Foster, 50
Duluth-Superior, 8, 133
Duplessis, Maurice, 37, 38, 66, 73, 74, 93, 107

Eisenhower, Dwight D., 33, 49, 50, 55, 60, 118, 146

147

Index

Eisenhower Lock, 77
Engineering Institute of Canada, 82
Erie Canal, 22, 23, 24, 25, 26, 116, 129

Fairweather, Starr, 68
Farran's Point, 108
Federal Power Commission, 50
Fort de Levis, 144
Fort William, 134
Frost, Leslie M., 29, 30, 37, 46, 55

Galop Island, 111
Galops Canal, 54
Galops Rapids, 111, 144
Gavsie, Charles, 52, 54, 61, 63, 67, 68, 75
Glover, T. R., 12
Gordon, Donald, 67, 68, 69, 70, 90
Grass River, 77
Great Lakes, 4, 5, 6, 7, 15, 16, 18, 19, 27, 34, 45, 116, 126, 130, 132, 135, 137
Great Lakes and Atlantic Canal and Power Company, 19
Great Lakes-St. Lawrence Basin Agreement, 32, 33, 40
Great Lakes Waterway Treaty, 32
Griffith, Ernest B., 134
Gut Dam, 36, 37, 111

Haldimand, General Frederick, 11
Hamilton, 134
Harrill, Reece, 120
Henry, R. A. C., 38, 50, 52, 53, 63
Holden, Dr. Otto, 76, 98
Honoré Mercier Bridge, 70, 72, 91
Howard Smith Paper Mills Ltd., 63
Howe, C. D., 29, 44, 47, 52, 55
Hudson's Bay Company, 24

Ingleside, 109, 143
International Joint Commission, 32, 33, 49, 53, 54

International Lake Level Board, 53, 54
International Rapids, 9, 29, 30, 31, 35, 36, 37, 40, 43, 47, 53, 61, 62, 64, 93, 97, 98, 104, 107
Iroquois, 54, 55, 62, 63, 64, 74, 95, 107, 108, 110, 143
Iroquois dam, 39, 95
Iroquois Indians, 106, 108
Iroquois Point, 54, 107

Jacques Cartier Bridge, 54, 65, 66, 67, 70, 72, 86, 87, 89, 90
Johnson's Mills, *see* St. Joseph
Johnston, Bill, 8, 143

Kingston, 8, 9, 25, 134, 141, 143

La Corporation du Pont du Lac St.-Louis, 71
Labrador, 7, 47, 116, 121, 130
Lachine, 19, 38, 47, 64, 73, 85, 90, 142
Lachine Canal, 15, 16, 20, 26, 27, 85, 104
Lachine Canal Company, 20
Lachine Rapids, 11, 12, 14, 36, 38, 85, 86, 89, 91, 142, 144, 145
Lake Carriers Association, 137
Lake Champlain, 17
Lake Erie, 6, 7, 8, 16, 17, 21, 26, 27, 35, 49, 89
Lake Huron, 7, 16, 17, 27, 35
Lake Michigan, 16, 17
Lake Ontario, 7, 8, 9, 11, 16, 17, 21, 22, 31, 35, 36, 37, 53, 95, 98, 111, 129
Lake St. Clair, 7
Lake St. Francis, 4, 11, 20, 35, 36, 92, 93, 111, 145
Lake St. John, 35
Lake St. Louis, 11, 20, 36, 89, 91, 92, 93, 104, 145
Lake Superior, 7, 16, 17, 35
Laprairie, 84, 86, 87
Laprairie Basin, 91
Leeds and Grenville Historical Society, 144
Lessard, Jean, 120

Long Sault (new town), 109, 143
Long Sault canal, 83
Long Sault Dam, 39, 95, 97
Long Sault Island, 94, 95, 97
Long Sault Rapids, 2, 3, 4, 9, 10, 11, 94, 95, 97, 144
Longueuil, 65
Lower Canada, 24, 26

Macdonell, Colonel "Red" George, 9
MacMillan, Norman, 68
Manicouagan River, 34, 35
Maritime Provinces, 135
Marler, George, 68
Massena, 44, 55, 60, 64, 77, 96, 123
Merritt, W. Hamilton, 20, 21, 22, 23, 25, 31
Mille Roches, 108
Milwaukee, 133
Mississippi River, 24, 116
Molson, John, 142
Montreal, 4, 5, 6, 9, 10, 24, 25, 26, 27, 31, 36, 37, 38, 49, 64, 65, 66, 71, 72, 73, 74, 84, 85, 87, 89, 90, 104, 115, 116, 124, 129, 130, 132, 133, 135, 138, 142, 144, 145
Montreal Harbour, 12, 36, 54, 86, 112
Montreal Light, Heat and Power Company, 92
Morrisburg, 108, 110, 143
Moses, Robert, 55, 77
Moulinette, 108, 109
Murphy, Gordon, 52, 75, 85, 105

National Harbours Board, 66, 67
National Research Council, 111, 112
New Iroquois, 109, 143
New York Central Railroad, 77, 93
New York City, 6, 23, 25, 116
New York Parks Commission, 143

New York State, 28, 35, 36, 56
Niagara, 21, 144
Niagara Falls, 35
Niagara River, 7, 21
North West Company, 24

Oettershagen, Martin W., 61
Ogdensburg, 9
Ohio River, 24
Ontario, steamer, 10
Ontario Hydro Electric Power Commission, 5, 28, 29, 30, 31, 33, 39, 43, 46, 55, 75, 76, 96, 97, 98, 104, 108, 109, 110, 111
Ontario-St. Lawrence Development Commission, 143
Oswego, 134, 144
Ottawa, 25
Ottawa River, 17, 34, 35, 36, 73, 92, 141

Panama Canal, 5, 7, 11, 17, 18, 19, 75, 76, 80, 93, 117, 123
Paterson, William, 17, 18
Pearson, Lester B., 33, 44, 45, 48, 50, 61, 62
Peribonka River, 35
Point Rockway, 63
Polly's Gut, 77, 78
Port Arthur, 134
Pouchot, Captain François, 144
Power Authority of the State of New York, 28, 32, 33, 39, 43, 50, 55, 75, 77, 96
Pratley, Dr. P. L., 88
Prescott, 8, 9, 36, 37, 111, 115, 130
Preville, 87
Prince, Gregory S., 128

Quebec City, 6, 10, 25, 132, 133, 142, 144
Quebec Hydro Electric Commission, 36, 38, 73

Rideau Canal, 22, 25, 142
Rivière St. Pierre, 15
Robert H. Saunders power-house, 28, 31

Index

Rock Island, 9
Romilly, Captain Samuel, 142
Royal Engineers, 20, 142

Saguenay River, 34, 35
St. Clair River, 7
St. Johns Railway, 84
St. Joseph, 18
St. Lambert, 86, 87, 89
St. Laurent, Louis, 29, 30, 33, 36, 37, 38, 42, 43, 44, 46, 49, 51, 55, 56, 60, 117, 145
St. Lawrence Board of Control, 53, 54
St. Lawrence Joint Board of Engineers, 32, 50, 53, 54
St. Lawrence Power Development Commission, see Power Authority of the State of New York
St. Lawrence River, 3, 4, 5, 6, 7, 14, 15, 16, 17, 19, 30, 32, 33, 34, 35, 39, 56, 93, 94, 111, 128, 129, 133, 134, 137, 138, 140, 146
St. Lawrence Seaway Authority, 5, 30, 39, 47, 51, 53, 54, 61, 63, 64, 66, 67, 71, 72, 73, 74, 81, 87, 88, 104, 106, 107, 118, 120, 122, 144, 145
St. Lawrence Seaway Authority Act, 47
St. Lawrence Seaway Development Corporation, 55, 58, 64, 98, 118, 120, 122
St. Lawrence State Park, 145
St. Lawrence Valley, 100, 143
St. Mary's Falls, 35
St. Mary's River, 7, 35
St. Maurice River, 34, 35
St. Regis, 77
Ste. Anne de Bellevue, 2
Sarnia, 134
Sault Ste. Marie Canals, 7, 27, 137
Saunders, Robert H., 30, 31, 33, 36, 55
Schwab, Charles, 18, 19
Seven Islands, 134
Sheek Island, 3, 9, 97, 107

Simcoe, Mrs. John Graves, 11
Six Nations Indians, see Iroquois Indians
Sorel, 133
Soulanges, 92
Soulanges Canal, 92
Soulanges Rapids, 92
Spencer Island, 37
Strait of Belle Isle, 8
Suez Canal, 5, 7, 19, 117, 123

Thousand Islands, 8, 94, 143
Toledo, 133
Toronto, 4, 6, 7, 132, 138
Toronto Harbour Commission, 134
Truman, Harry S., 33, 45, 46, 48, 49
Twelve Mile Creek, 21, 22

United Empire Loyalists, 40, 108, 144
Upper Canada, 24, 25, 26, 129, 131
Upper Canada Village, 143

Valleyfield, 133
Verdun, 85
Victoria Bridge, 38, 54, 66, 67, 68, 69, 70, 89, 90
Ville St. Pierre, 70
Von Schoultz, Colonel, 9

Wales, 108
War of 1812, 9, 20, 26
Welland Canal, 17, 23, 26, 27, 52, 76, 85, 99, 111, 116, 119, 120, 128, 136
Welland Canal Company, 22, 23
Welland River, 21, 22
Wellesley Island, 8
Wershof, Max, 61
West, C. W., 52, 54, 61, 63, 75
Wiley, Alexander, 118, 119
Wiley-Dondero Act, 50, 52
Wilson, Norman D., 40
Windsor, 17, 27, 134
Wooten, Lt.-Col. W. P., 31, 32, 40

Index

THE ST. LAWRENCE

SEAWAY

IN MAPS AND PICTURES

1 Hamilton
2 St. Catharines
3 Welland Canal
4 Welland
5 Niagara Falls, Ontario
6 Niagara Falls, N.Y.
7 Buffalo, N.Y.
8 Toronto
9 Oshawa
10 Port Hope
11 Cobourg
12 Trenton
13 Belleville
14 Kingston
15 Brockville
16 Prescott
17 Ogdensburg, N.Y.
18 Iroquois Lock and Canal
19 Iroquois

ONTARIO

LAKE ONTARIO

continued ▶

AKE
RIE

THE WESTERN SECTION: WELLAND TO PRESCOTT

151

Maps and Pictures

(see also page 166)

20 Iroquois Dam
21 Morrisburg
22 Ingleside
23 Long Sault Island
24 Long Sault
25 Long Sault Dam
26 Eisenhower and Snell Locks
27 Massena, N.Y.
28 Sheek Island
29 Barnhart Island
30 International Power Houses
31 Cornwall International High-Level Bridge
32 Cornwall
33 Cornwall Island

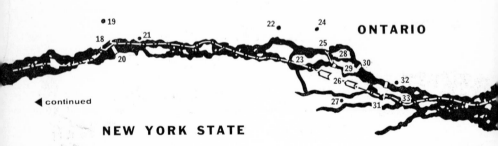

152

Maps and Pictures

34 Beauharnois Canal
35 Soulanges Canal
36 Beauharnois Locks
37 Beauharnois
38 Caughnawaga
39 Lachine
40 C.P.R. Caughnawaga Bridge
41 Honoré Mercier Bridge
42 Côte Ste. Catherine Lock
43 Victoria Bridge
44 Laprairie
45 Jacques Cartier Bridge
46 Montreal
47 St. Lambert Lock
48 St. Lambert

153

Maps

"The Seaway channel begins at Jacques Cartier Bridge. . . . Behind the graceful rise of the bridge lies a fascinating story of human ingenuity." (Page 87)

154

Maps and Pictures

Before and after "jacking up several thousand tons of bridge."
(Page 87)

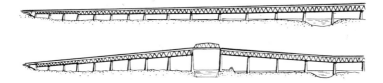

155

The Entrance

156

Maps and Pictures

"The problem of the Victoria Bridge. . . . The solution was simple but expensive." (Page 69)

TRAFFIC FLOW AT ST. LAMBERT LOCK

"It is interesting to imagine a ship going through this lock. . . ." The lower bridge approach is temporary; to be replaced by one "that moves out across the water diagonally. . . ." (Page 91)

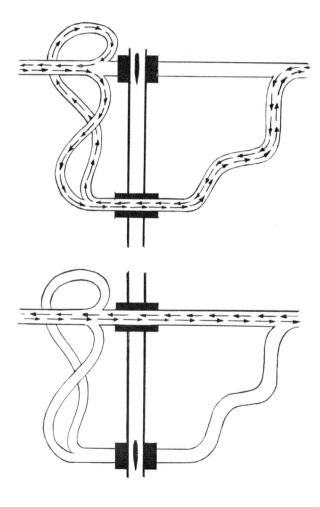

157

St. Lambert Lock

". . . in the distance two bridges can be seen, the Honoré Mercier and a C.P.R. bridge." (Page 91)

158

Maps and Pictures

THE HONORÉ MERCIER BRIDGE (RIGHT) AND C.P.R. CAUGHNAWAGA BRIDGE (LEFT)

"Construction problems here were not so acute as lower down the river." (Page 91)

More Bridges

AT THE FOOT OF LAKE ST. LOUIS
"On the right of the seaway channel, going upriver, the foaming white-caps of the Lachine Rapids can be seen and the canal is nearly ready to let the ship onto Lake St. Louis." (Page 91)

RIGHT: BEAUHARNOIS (1)
". . . we had to build two locks alongside the Beauharnois power-house. . . . It was here that contractors struck the fault of sandstone and wore out so much of their equipment." (Page 93)

160

Maps and Pictures

161

Beauharnois

162

Maps and Pictures

Left to right: The Honourable George C. Marler, Minister of Transport; The Honourable Wilber M. Brucker, Secretary of the Army (U.S.A.); The Honourable Lionel Chevrier, President of the St. Lawrence Seaway Authority; Mr. Lewis G. Castle, Administrator of the St. Lawrence Seaway Development Corporation (U.S.A.)

LEFT: BEAUHARNOIS (2)
"Apart from the problems of the rock in this area, the other difficulties were routine. The contractors had to move about 750,000 cubic yards of concrete, build a four-lane highway tunnel under the lower lock. . . ." (Page 93)

BELOW: THE NEW CORNWALL INTERNATIONAL HIGH-LEVEL BRIDGE.

Officials and Cornwall

THE INTERNATIONAL POWER PROJECT, BARNHART ISLAND, AND LONG
SAULT DAM (LEFT BACKGROUND)

". . . providing a vast quantity of cheap power." (Page 96)

164

Maps and Pictures

165

The International Power Project

". . . for the Hydro men it was the biggest moment in the commission's history." (Page 98)

THE INTERNATIONAL SECTION

". . . the area in which the work was done extended from Cornwall up the river for fifty miles." (Page 94)

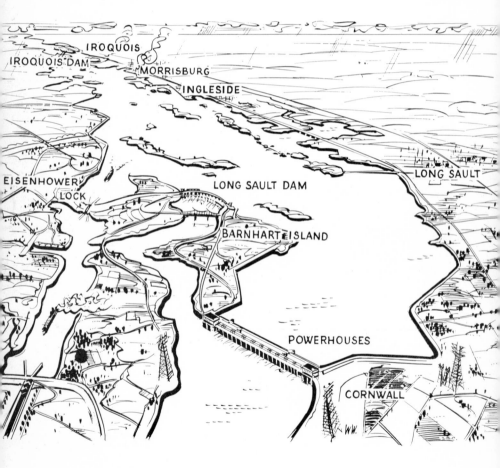

166

Maps and Pictures

". . . the bulk of the work is left behind once Iroquois and its dam and the Canadian lock are passed." (Page 98)

168

Maps and Pictures

169

The Lock at Iroquois

PERSUADING THE IROQUOIS

"When it came to my turn I took a good pull at it. . . ." (Page 106)

LEFT: MOVING THE PEOPLE: IROQUOIS

"The old village of Iroquois moved its first house in the fall of 1955
. . . to the new location about a mile north." (Page 110)

Moving the People

RIGHT: MODEL OF THE CORNWALL AREA

"The models repaid their investment costs many times over." (Page 112)

MOVING THE PEOPLE: MORRISBURG

"The largest community affected by the flooding was Morrisburg." (Page 110)

172

Maps and Pictures

173

The Models

".. . much of the excavation work was done in winter when the canal was drained." (Page 99)

CREDITS

photographs

154, 156, 158, 159, 160, 161, 162, 163 top:
St. Lawrence Seaway Authority and Hans Van der Aa

163 lower: Power Authority, State of New York

164, 168, 170, 172: Ontario Hydro

167: Canadian Industries Limited

171: Gazette Photo Service

173: Capital Press

174: Don Sinclair

Maps and diagrams by William Wheeler

174

Maps and Pictures